READ WELL Plus

My Activity Book 5

Units 39-50

Comprehension and Skill Work

Sopris West™
EDUCATIONAL SERVICES

A Cambium Learning Company

BOSTON, MA · LONGMONT, CO

ISBN 1-59318-544-8
Printed in the United States of America
Published and Distributed by

Sopris West™
EDUCATIONAL SERVICES

A Cambium Learning Company

4093 Specialty Place • Longmont, CO 80504 • 303-651-2829

www.sopriswest.com

ILLUSTRATION CREDITS

Cover   Storybook 50 image by Ashley Mims.

Unit 39   1, 2: Bear, chipmunk illustrated by Chi Chung. 4: Chipmunk ©Jupiter Images. 8: Bear ©Jupiter Images. 12: Bear illustrated by Chi Chung; tree illustrated by Mr. E-Men. Storybook illustrated by Chi Chung.

Unit 40   13: Desert, rainforest ©Jupiter Images. 16: Camel ©Jupiter Images. 20: Camel illustrated by Dan McGeehan. Storybook illustrated by Dan McGeehan.

Unit 41   Desert, rainforest ©Jupiter Images. 32: Sloth illustrated by Eldon Doty. Storybook illustrated by Eldon Doty.

Unit 42   38: Mouse, faces ©Jupiter Images; elephant illustrated by Burgandy Beam. 43: Bike ©Jupiter Images. Storybook illustrated by Selina Alko.

Unit 43   Storybook illustrated by Cindy Revell.

Unit 44   61: Flashlight ©Jupiter Images. 62: Trapdoor illustrated by Cindy Revell; secret passage ©Jupiter Images. 63: Footprints ©Jupiter Images. 64: Magnifying glass ©Jupiter Images. 65: Carlos illustrated by Selina Alko; Maya illustrated by Cindy Revell. 66: Shovel ©Jupiter Images. 67: Magnifying glass, hat ©Jupiter Images.

Unit 45   75: Desert, rainforest, hats, faces ©Jupiter Images. 76, 77, 79: Frogs illustrated by Burgandy Beam. 84: Frog, letters ©Jupiter Images. Storybook illustrated by Burgandy Beam.

Unit 46   87: Frog illustrated by Burgandy Beam. 88: Frogs illustrated by Burgandy Beam. 89: Plants illustrated by Burgandy Beam. 92: List in garden illustrated by Burgandy Beam. 95: Cookies ©Jupiter Images.

Unit 47   100: Octopus ©Jupiter Images. 104: Jellyfish ©Jupiter Images. Storybook illustrated by Fabricio VandenBroeck.

Unit 48   109: Solar system, courtesy of NASA. 110: Astronaut ©Jupiter Images. 111: Space shuttle ©Jupiter Images. 112: Space station ©Jupiter Images. 113: Space station, courtesy of NASA. 114: Space probe ©Digital Stock. 116: Sedna, courtesy of NASA. 117: Solar system, courtesy of NASA. 118: Space station, courtesy of NASA. 119: Astronauts ©Jupiter Images. 120: All images ©Jupiter Images.

Unit 49   128: Asteroid ©Jupiter Images. Storybook illustrated by Ka Botzis.

Unit 50   136: Reptiles illustrated by Ka Botzis. 140: Scientist ©Jupiter Images. 141: Building illustrated by Ka Botzis. 144: Dinosaur illustrated by Ka Botzis; satellite, dinosaur tracks, planet ©Jupiter Images. Storybook illustrated by Ashley Mims.

Table of Contents

Unit 39 Activity 1
For use after Exercise 1 and Story 1

Name _____

Story Comprehension
How the Chipmunk Got His Stripes, Chapter 1

★1 **Which animal is big and which animal is little?**

★ The opposite of <u>big</u> is little.

○ big   ○ little   ○ big   ○ little

---

2 **Who first told this story?**
○ American bears   ○ American Indians   ○ American chipmunks

3 **This story is about** _____
○ Bear and Chipmunk   ○ logs and rocks   ○ big black chipmunks

4 **Where does the story take place?**

This story takes place _____

5 **What did Bear say when he was bragging?**
○ Bear said, "I am too small. I just can't do anything."
○ Bear growled, "I am so strong, there is nothing I cannot do."

6 **Chipmunk said, "Bear thinks he is _____ because he is big."**
○ foolish   ○ important   ○ nothing

7 **What foolish thing did Chipmunk say to Bear?**
○ "I am important."   ○ "I'm big and strong."   ○ "Is that so?"

Unit 39 Activity 2
For use after Exercise 2 and Story 2

Name _____

Story Comprehension
How the Chipmunk Got His Stripes, Chapter 2

1 Who is the story about? (Start with *The story is about . . .*)

_____

_____

2 What was Bear doing when he said, "I am so strong, there is nothing I cannot do"?

○ humming   ○ singing   ○ bragging

3 Why did Bear pick up a rock and toss it?

○ Bear wanted Chipmunk to see how strong he was.

○ Bear wanted Chipmunk to run down the hill.

4 Why did Bear think Chipmunk should be afraid of him?

○ One animal was afraid of him.

○ All the other animals were afraid of him.

5 What did Chipmunk ask Bear to do?

Chipmunk asked Bear to stop _____

_____

6 Write one sentence about Bear. (Start with *Bear . . .*)

_____

7 Which animal is big and which animal is little?

The opposite of <u>little</u> is <u>big</u>.

○ big   ○ little   ○ big   ○ little

Unit 39 Activity 3
For use as appropriate

Name _____

★ Rhyming Words

Fill in the bubble next to the word that rhymes. The first one is done for you.

1. **claws**	● paws	○ arms	○ feet
2. **tumble**	○ talk	○ sing	○ grumble
3. **blink**	○ trick	○ wink	○ tear
4. **howl**	○ dog	○ growl	○ sound

★ Rhyming Poem

Read each sentence and find the word that rhymes with the underlined word and makes sense. Fill in the bubble and write the word on the line.

1 **The bear has sharp <u>claws</u>**

on his big, strong _____ .

○ paws   ○ feet   ○ arms

2 **When Chipmunk falls and takes a <u>tumble</u>,**

he will squeak, and he will _____ .

○ talk   ○ sing   ○ grumble

3 **Did you see Chipmunk <u>blink</u>?**

No, I think it was a _____ .

○ trick   ○ wink   ○ tear

4 **Did you hear Bear <u>howl</u>?**

No, I think it was a _____ .

○ growl   ○ sound   ○ dog

5 **From a tall tree, Chipmunk could <u>hear</u>**

that bear was _____ .

○ fat   ○ fear   ○ near

3

Name _____

★ Main Idea and Supporting Details

Chipmunks in Winter

In the winter, it is hard for chipmunks to find food. What do the little animals do? All spring, summer, and fall, little chipmunks look for food. The chipmunks carry food in their cheeks. Then they store their food in tunnels. If you see a chipmunk with fat cheeks, it is getting ready for the long, cold winter.

1 **What do chipmunks do in the spring, summer, and fall?**

First they _____

○ play in the pool   ○ look for food   ○ take a nap

2 **How do the chipmunks carry food back to their tunnels?**

They carry food _____

○ in their cheeks   ○ in their paws   ○ on their backs

3 **Where do chipmunks store food for the winter?**

They store food _____

○ in their desks   ○ in the winter   ○ in tunnels

4 **When chipmunks look for food, carry food in their cheeks, and put food underground, they are . . .**

_____

○ getting ready for winter   ○ getting ready to cook a great meal

Unit 39 Activity 5
For use after Exercise 3 and Story 3

Name _____

★ Sentence Jumble

Use the words in each box to make a sentence. Start each sentence with a capital letter. End each sentence with a period.

| chipmunk small was | _____ _____ |

| big bear was | _____ _____ |

| bragged bear the | _____ _____ |

| chipmunk the yawned | _____ _____ |

Read the sentences. Do they make sense?

Name _____

★Alphabetical Order and My Picture Dictionary

1. Fill in the missing letters of the alphabet in the first column.
2. Read the definitions of the words.
   Then write at least one more fact about bears and chipmunks.
3. Draw a picture of the word in the box.

A
B

D
E

G
H

J
K

M
N

P
Q

S
T

V
W

Y
Z

bear
A bear is a mammal. Bears have thick fur.

Bears _____

_____

_____

chipmunk
A chipmunk is a mammal.

Chipmunks _____

_____

_____

mammal
A mammal is a kind of animal. All mammals have a backbone. They breathe air. They take care of their babies, and they have hair or fur. Bears, chipmunks, and people are mammals.

Name _____

★ Characterization

Foolish Bear

Bear sat all night waiting for the sun to come up. When the sun began to rise, Bear growled, "It is I. It is Bear. Listen to what I have to say. Sun, do not shine today!" Bear was foolish!

1 Bear was big and strong.
Did that make him foolish?   yes   no

2 Bear thought he could do anything.
Did that make him foolish?   yes   no

3 Bear was big and strong, so he ate a lot.
Did that make him foolish?   yes   no

4 Bear said, "Sun, do not shine today!"
Did that make him foolish?   yes   no

You should have two "yes" answers.

Name _____

Main Idea and Supporting Details

Bears in Winter

During the cold winter, bears like to sleep. But, what do they do for food? In the late summer, bears get very hungry. They eat little ants, small animals, fish, nuts, and grasses. By winter, the bears have become very full. When it gets cold, the bears crawl into their dens. They are so fat they can sleep all winter without eating.

1 **What do bears do in the winter?**

They _____

○ eat good snacks   ○ look for food   ○ sleep without eating

2 **In the late summer bears get hungry. List three things bears will eat.**

- _____

- _____

- _____

3 **By winter, bears are** _____

○ full and skinny   ○ full and fat   ○ hungry and fat

4 **When bears eat and get fat, they are getting** _____

○ ready for a run   ○ ready to sleep

Name _____

Characterization

Foolish Chipmunk

The sun did not listen to Bear. It rose high in the sky and made daylight.
Bear was angry. Chipmunk thought it was funny, so he laughed at Bear.
Chipmunk was foolish!

1   Chipmunk was a small, furry animal.
        Did that make him foolish?   yes   no

2   Chipmunk laughed at Bear.
        Did that make him foolish?   yes   no

3   Chipmunk sang, "Tee hee, tee hee,
        The sun is up. The sun is high in the sky."
        Did that make him foolish?   yes   no

4   Chipmunk laughed so hard he fell down.
        Did that make him foolish?   yes   no

You should have three "yes" answers.

Unit 39 Activity 10
For use after Exercise 6 and Story 6

Name _____

Story Map
How the Chipmunk Got His Stripes

SETTING

When

| Long ago |

Where

| |

MAIN CHARACTERS

Bear

_____

_____

Problem

Bragged too much

Chipmunk

_____

_____

Problem

_____

● **BEGINNING**

Bear bragged. He said, "_____

_____

■ **MIDDLE** • Action

Bear said that he could stop the sun from coming up, but the sun

_____

▲ **END** • Conclusion

Chipmunk _____ Bear.
○ laughed at   ○ smiled at   ○ hugged

When Chipmunk tried to run away, Bear _____

_____

○ scratched his head   ○ scratched Chipmunk's back   ○ chuckled

Unit 39 Activity 11
For use after Exercise 6 and Story 6

Name _____

★ Written Retell
How the Chipmunk Got His Stripes

Tell where the story took place. Tell who the main characters were and a little about each character. (You may want to start with *Long ago . . .*)

_____

_____

_____

_____

_____

● **BEGINNING** • Read what happened at the beginning of the story.

Bear bragged. He said, "I can do anything."

■ **MIDDLE** • Tell what happened in the middle of the story.
You may wish to add details that weren't on the story map.

Bear said that he could stop the sun from coming up, but the sun

_____

_____

▲ **END** • Tell how the story ended.

Chipmunk _____ Bear. When Chipmunk tried

to run away, Bear _____

_____

_____

Unit 39 Activity 12
For use as appropriate

Name _____

Take-Home Game
★Rhyming Pairs

Start

fat

light

ray

Go back two.

can

sun

hear

fine

Materials
Game markers
Die (or Number Cards 1–6)

Game Directions
This game can be played with two or three players.
1. The player rolls the die and then moves his or her marker the number rolled on the die. (If the player rolls a six, the player moves six spaces.)
2. The player says a word (or nonsense word) that rhymes with the word in the space where he or she landed. If the player lands in a space with a star, the player says a rhyming word and then moves forward one space.

Alternative: The player draws a number card instead of using a die. Number cards 1–6. Make at least three cards of each number. Shuffle the cards and place the cards upside down in a draw pile.

fun

fear

Go back three.

fool

★saw

★claw

pan

bright

What does a <u>bear</u> <u>wear</u>?

★<u>p</u><u>aw</u>

way

rat

Go back one.

shine

cool

flight

End

12

Unit 40 Activity 1
For use after Exercise 1 and Story 1

Name _____

Story Comprehension
How the Camel Got His Hump, Chapter 1

1 Which habitat is wet and which is dry?

Desert

Rain Forest

The opposite of <u>wet</u> is dry.

○ wet   ○ dry   ○ wet   ○ dry

---

2 What does the story explain? (Start with *The story explains . . .*)

_____

_____

3 Where does the story take place?

The story takes place _____

○ in a forest   ○ in the jungle   ○ in a desert

4 Describe the desert.

○ A desert is dry.   ○ A desert is wet.   ○ A desert is full of trees.

5 When does the story take place? The story takes place . . .

○ when the world was old.   ○ when the world was new.

6 Describe the camel.

○ The camel was the laziest of all the animals.

○ The camel was the smartest of all the animals.

Unit 40 Activity 2
For use after Exercise 2 and Story 2

Name _____

Story Comprehension
How the Camel Got His Hump, Chapter 2

This story is about four animals who live in the desert.

★1 <u>Describe</u> Horse.

    ○ Horse worked hard. He had a saddle on his back to carry the man.

    ○ Horse was lazy. He did not like to work.

2 Describe Dog.

    ○ Dog was lazy. He did not like to work.

    ○ Dog worked hard. He would fetch and carry for the man.

3 Describe Ox.

    ○ Ox worked hard. He would pull a plow for the man.

    ○ Ox did not work hard. He was the laziest of all the animals.

4 Describe Camel.

    ○ Camel worked hard. He would carry the man on his back, fetch and carry, and plow for the man.

    ○ Camel did not work hard. He was the laziest of all the animals.

5 What was the problem? Camel wouldn't work, so Man said the others . . .

    ○ could rest.   ○ had to work harder.

6 Which animals were lazy and which were hard-working?

  ○ lazy   ○ lazy   ○ lazy   ○ lazy

  ○ hard-working   ○ hard-working   ○ hard-working   ○ hard-working

7 The opposite of *hard-working* is _____

Name _____

★ Following Directions
Table of Contents

1 Look at the Table of Contents. Write "camel" under the picture of the camel.

2 Underline the name of the story.

3 Draw an X on the word "Introduction."

4 Which page does Chapter 6 start on?

    ○ 26

    ○ 33

    ○ 36

5 Which page does Chapter 2 start on?

    ○ 26

    ○ 28

    ○ 36

6 Your story is called "How the Camel Got His Hump." This story could also be called . . .

    ○ "The Rude, Lazy Camel."

    ○ "The Hard-Working, Wise Camel."

UNIT 40 STORY

How the Camel Got His Hump

Name _____

Main Idea and Supporting Details

Camels in the Desert

Camels are perfect for living in the desert. These big animals store food in their humps, so they can walk across the desert for days without food or water.

The desert sand can be a problem for many animals, but not for camels. They have flat, wide feet to keep them from sinking into the sand. They have long eyelashes to keep sand out of their eyes. They can even close their nostrils to keep the sand out of their noses.

1 **Where do camels live?**

They _____
○ live in the rain forest   ○ live in the dry desert   ○ live in the creeks

2 **Camels are perfect for desert life. What makes camels perfect for desert life?**

• Camels have flat, wide feet   → to keep them from _____

_____

• Camels have long eyelashes   → to keep sand _____

_____

• Camels can close their nostrils → to keep the sand _____

_____

★3 **What is the *whole* story about?**
○ Camels have wide feet.
○ Camels are perfect for living in a desert habitat.

Unit 40 Activity 5
For use after Exercise 3 and Story 3

Name _____

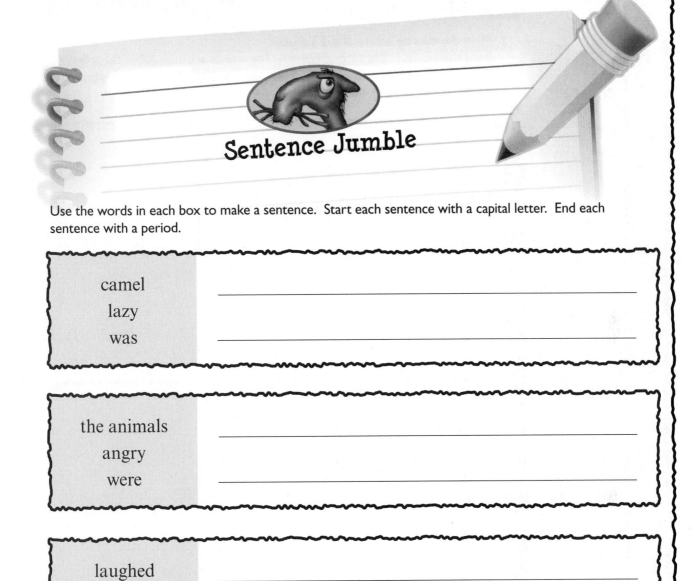

Sentence Jumble

Use the words in each box to make a sentence. Start each sentence with a capital letter. End each sentence with a period.

camel lazy was	_____ _____

the animals angry were	_____ _____

laughed camel the	_____ _____

whistled genie the	_____ _____

Read the sentences. Do they make sense?

Unit 40 Activity 6
For use after Exercise 4 and Story 4

Name _____

Alphabetical Order and My Picture Dictionary

1. Fill in the missing letters of the alphabet.
   Read the words in the second column. The words are in alphabetical order.
2. Read the definitions of the words. Then write at least one more fact about each word.
3. Draw a picture of the word in the box.

A
B
camel
D
dog
E

G
H
horse

J
K

M
N
ox
P
Q

S
T

V
W

Y
Z

camel
A camel is a mammal. Camels are perfect for living in the desert.

They _____

_____

_____

dog
A dog is a mammal. Dogs are often called man's best friend.

They _____

_____

_____

horse
A horse is a mammal. Horses are big, strong animals.

They _____

_____

_____

Name _____

Characterization

The Rude Camel

When Man asked Camel to work, Camel just said, "Humph." When Horse, Dog, and Ox asked Camel to help them, Camel just said, "Humph." When the genie asked Camel why he did no work, Camel just said, "Humph." Camel was not only lazy. He was also rude.

1 Camel lived in the desert.
Did that make him rude?   yes   no

2 Camel ate sticks, thorns, and milkweed.
Did that make him rude?   yes   no

3 Whenever someone asked Camel to work, he just said, "Humph."
Did that make him rude?   yes   no

4 When the genie asked Camel why he didn't work, Camel said "Humph."
Did that make him rude?   yes   no

You should have two "yes" answers.

Name _____

Main Idea and Supporting Details

What Are Camels?

Are camels fish? No. Camels do not have gills. Are camels birds? No. Camels do not have feathers. Are camels insects? No. Camels do not have six legs. What are camels? Camels are mammals. Just like people, bears, and chipmunks, camels take care of their babies. They have backbones. Like all mammals, camels also breathe air and have hair.

1 The main idea is camels are mammals.
List four facts that tell you camels are mammals.

They _____

They _____

They _____

They _____

2 What's the main idea? (Start with *Camels are . . .*)

_____

3 Write at least two sentences about camels.

_____

_____

_____

Unit 40 Activity 9
For use after Exercise 5 and Story 5

Name _____

★ Visualizing and Illustrating
How the Camel Got His Hump, Chapter 5

Read and illustrate the story below.

1 Long, long ago, a rude and most lazy camel lived in the desert. When the other animals worked, Camel just said, "Humph."	**2** Man said that Horse, Dog, and Ox would all have to work harder. This made the animals angry.
3 Finally, the genie asked Camel to work, but Camel just said, "Humph."	**4** The desert genie gave Camel a great lolloping humph on his back. Then the genie told Camel he would have to work.

5 **Do you think Camel learned to work hard?**   yes   no

6 **Do you think Camel is still lazy and rude?**   yes   no

Unit 40 Activity 10
For use after Exercise 6 and Story 6

Name _____

Story Map
How the Camel Got His Hump

SETTING • Tell when and where the story took place.

When

Where

MAIN CHARACTER • Tell who the story is about and something about the character.

_____

_____

● **BEGINNING** • Tell how the story started.

Horse, Dog, and Ox all _____

_____

① Horse asked Camel to come out and trot, but Camel said, "Humph."

② Dog asked Camel to fetch, but _____

③ Ox asked Camel to plow, _____

■ **MIDDLE** • Tell about Horse, Dog, and Ox's problem.

Man said that Horse, Dog, and Ox would all need to work harder because

_____

▲ **END** • Tell what happened to Camel.

Camel said, "_____" one too many times, so the genie

_____

○ watched   ○ gave Camel a hump   ○ said "Humph" back

Unit 40 Activity 11
For use after Exercise 6 and Story 6

Name _____

Written Retell
How the Camel Got His Hump

Tell when and where the story took place. Tell who the main character was and a little about him.

_____

_____

● **BEGINNING** • Tell how the story started.

Horse, Dog, and Ox all _____

_____

_____

■ **MIDDLE** • Tell about the problem.

Man said that Horse, Dog, and Ox would all need to work harder because

_____

▲ **END** • Tell how the story ended and explain what camels do now.

Camel said, "_____" one too many times, so

the genie _____

Now, camels _____

_____

★ **STORY RESPONSE** • Start with *I liked the story because . . .* or *I didn't like the story because . . .*

_____

_____

Name _____

Rhyming Words

Fill in the bubble next to the word that rhymes. The first one is done for you.

1. **new**	● drew	○ draw	○ now
2. **prickles**	○ pushes	○ grumbles	○ pickles
3. **howling**	○ hopping	○ growling	○ sinking
4. **howl**	○ growl	○ dog	○ sound

Rhyming Poem

Find the rhyming word that makes sense for each sentence. Fill in the bubble and write the word on the line.

1 **When the camel was <u>new</u>,**

He grew and _____ .
○ ran   ○ grew   ○ laughed

2 **He really liked <u>prickles</u>,**

But did not like _____ .
○ sand   ○ grass   ○ pickles

3 **When the desert would <u>howl</u>,**

The camel would _____ .
○ growl   ○ sink   ○ hop

4 **He'd grumble and <u>mumble</u>,**

and his tummy would _____ .
○ snort   ○ laugh   ○ rumble

5 **Then he'd eat <u>sticks</u>,**

And a few little _____ .
○ ants   ○ eggs   ○ bricks

Name _____

Story Comprehension
Why the Sloth Is Slow, Chapter 1

1 Which habitat is dry
and which is wet?

Desert   **Rain Forest**

> The
> opposite of
> <u>dry</u> is <u>wet</u>.

○ wet   ○ dry   ○ wet   ○ dry

2 **Who is the story about?** (Start with *The story is about . . .*)

_____

3 **What does the story explain?** (Start with *The story explains . . .*)

_____

_____

4 **Where does the story take place?**

The story takes place _____
○ in a rain forest   ○ in a school   ○ in a desert

5 **When does the story take place? The story takes place . . .**
○ when Jessica was ten.   ○ long ago.

6 **This is the beginning of the story. Describe Sloth.**
○ Sloth was the slowest of all the animals.
○ Sloth was the quickest of all the animals.

Name _____

Story Comprehension
Why the Sloth Is Slow, Chapter 2

1 **Who is the story about?** Write two sentences about Sloth. (Start with *The story is about . . .*)

_____

_____

Rhyming Poem

Words that rhyme all end the same. Read each sentence and find the word that rhymes with the underlined word and makes sense. Fill in the bubble and write the word on the line.

2 **Can you see me swing in the <u>trees</u>,**

Or do you only feel a passing _____ ?
○ breeze   ○ wind   ○ tease

3 **I move so fast that you do not <u>see</u>,**

That wind you feel is really _____ .
○ Sloth   ○ me   ○ a bee

4 **I run all day and run all <u>night</u>,**

And when I'm done it's only _____ ,
○ happy   ○ dark   ○ right

5 **To eat and eat my <u>fill</u>,**

And that's the only time I'm _____ .
○ well   ○ happy   ○ still

Name _____

Following Directions
Table of Contents

1 Look at the Table of Contents. Draw an X on the word "New."

2 Draw a line under the picture of Jaguar.

3 Find "Chapter 3." What page is Chapter 3 found on?

    ◯ 44

    ◯ 47

    ◯ 49

4 Draw a box around the <u>ow</u> in "Slow."

5 Chapter 7 is found on page . . .

    ◯ 49.

    ◯ 41.

    ◯ 57.

6 Your story is called "Why the Sloth Is Slow." This story could also be called . . .

    ◯ "Speed Up, Sloth."

    ◯ "Slow Down, Sloth."

TABLE OF CONTENTS
UNIT 41 • A New Story

Why the Sloth Is Slow

Name _____

Main Idea and Supporting Details

More About Anacondas

Anacondas are the biggest snakes in the world. They live in the rain forests of South America. These big snakes grow to be very long. In fact, an anaconda can grow to be as long as a school bus.

Anacondas live near streams, watching and waiting for their next meal. Some anacondas are so big they can eat pigs, deer, and even jaguars. One of the biggest anacondas ever seen was 28 feet long and 44 inches around.

1 **What is the story about?** (Start with *The story is about . . .*)

_____

2 **One way to say the main idea is "Anacondas are the biggest snakes in the world." List three facts that tell you that anacondas are big.**

Anacondas may grow to be as long as a _____

They are so big, they can eat _____

One of the biggest anacondas ever seen was _____

3 **What's one way to say the main idea?** (Start with *Anacondas . . .*)

_____

4 **Write at least two sentences about anacondas.** (Start with your main idea.)

_____

_____

Unit 41 Activity 5
For use as appropriate

Name _____

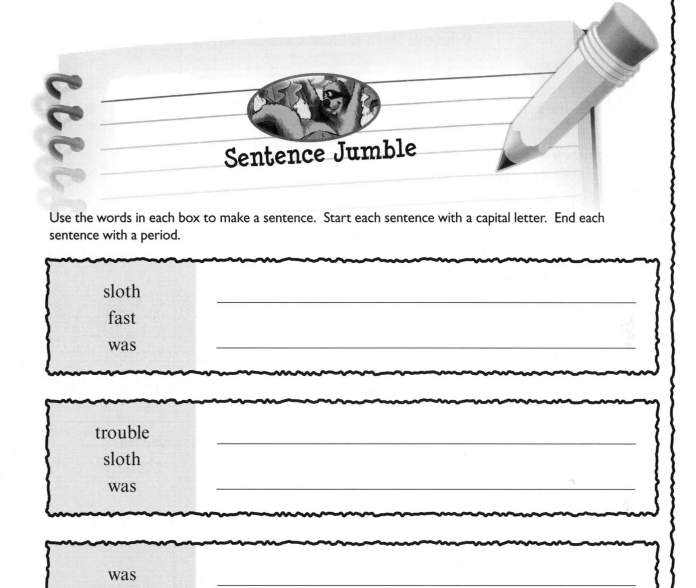

Sentence Jumble

Use the words in each box to make a sentence. Start each sentence with a capital letter. End each sentence with a period.

sloth fast was	_____ _____

trouble sloth was	_____ _____

was greedy sloth	_____ _____

a problem was sloth	_____ _____

Read the sentences. Do they make sense?

Unit 41 Activity 6
For use after Exercise 4 and Story 4

Name _____

Visualizing and Illustrating
Why the Sloth Is Slow, Chapter 4

Read and illustrate the story below.

1 Long, long ago, a rude and fast-moving sloth lived in the rain forest.	**2** Sloth never sat still. She would eat everything in sight.
3 The animals of the rain forest met. They needed a plan to slow Sloth down.	**4** Soon the animals were busy. They cut and tied vines with small bows.

5 **Do you think Sloth will learn to slow down?**   yes   no

Name _____

Characterization

The Greedy Sloth

From the day she was born, Sloth never sat still. The greedy sloth ate everything in sight. The animals worried that Sloth would eat and eat until the rain forest was gone.

1 Sloth lived in the rain forest.
Did that make her greedy?   yes   no

2 Sloth never sat still.
Did that make her greedy?   yes   no

3 Sloth ate everything in sight.
Did that make her greedy?   yes   no

4 Sloth liked to sing a song.
Did that make her greedy?   yes   no

You should have one "yes" answer.

Name _____

Main Idea and Supporting Details

More About Sloths

Sloths are the slowest, laziest mammals on Earth. They spend most of their day sleeping upside down in the trees. When these animals are awake, everything they do takes a long time. When sloths crawl down to the ground, it takes them an hour just to get there!

At night, they eat leaves and small twigs, but they don't eat a lot because they are so slow. In fact, sloths are so slow and lazy that little green plants grow in their fur!

1 **What is the story about?**

The story is about _____
○ the rain forest   ○ sloths   ○ green plants

2 **Sloths are the slowest, laziest mammals on Earth.**

• Sloths are so slow and lazy, ⟶ it takes an hour to climb down

_____

• Sloths are so slow and lazy, ⟶ they don't need_____

_____

• Sloths are so slow and lazy, ⟶ little green plants_____

_____

3 **What is the *whole* story about?**

○ Sloths are the slowest, laziest mammals on Earth.

○ Sloths are the slowest insects on Earth.

Unit 41 Activity 9
For use after Exercise 5 and Story 5

Name _____

Alphabetical Order and My Picture Dictionary

A
B
D
E
G
H
J
K
M
N
P
Q
S
T
V
W
Y
Z

anaconda

ja_ _ _ _ _

s_ _ _ _ _

1. Fill in the missing letters of the alphabet.
   Complete the words in the second column and then read them.
2. Read the definitions of the words. Then write at least one more fact about each word.
3. Draw a picture of the word in the box.

anaconda
An anaconda is an animal, but it is not a mammal.

Anacondas _____

_____

_____

jaguar
A jaguar is a mammal. Jaguars are big, spotted cats.

Jaguars _____

_____

_____

sloth
A sloth is a mammal.

Sloths _____

_____

_____

Name _____

Story Map
Why the Sloth Is Slow

SETTING · Tell when and where the story took place.

When

Where

MAIN CHARACTER · Tell who the story is about and something about the character.

_____ _____

● **BEGINNING** · Tell how the story started.

One day _____

Tell about the problem.
The animals thought Sloth would eat until the rain forest was gone.

Sloth_____

■ **MIDDLE** · Action

Jag gathered all the animals of the rain forest. Each animal had a plan to slow Sloth down. Anaconda's plan was to steal all the leaves.

Turtle's plan was _____

Jaguar's plan was _____

▲ **END**

When Sloth swished in the trees, she landed on the ground with a thump.

Sloth learned_____
○ to listen   ○ to move slowly   ○ to sing

Unit 41 Activity 11
For use after Exercise 6 and Story 6

Name _____

Written Retell
Why the Sloth Is Slow

Tell when and where the story took place. Introduce and describe the main character.

_____

_____

_____

● **BEGINNING** • Tell how the story started and a little about the problem.

_____

_____

_____

■ **MIDDLE** • Tell what the rain forest animals did to solve the problem.

Jag _____

_____

_____

▲ **END** • Tell how the story ended and explain what Sloth learned.

_____

_____

Sloth learned _____

STORY RESPONSE • Start with *I liked the story because . . .* or *I didn't like the story because . . .*

_____

_____

_____

Name _____

Take-Home Game
Rhyming Pairs

Start

rain

★ drew

drain

grew

Go back to "drew."

run

flew

ground

sun

sound

Materials:
Game markers   Die (or Number Cards 1–6)

Game Directions:
This game can be played with two or three players.

1. The player rolls the die, then moves his/her marker the number rolled on the die, reading the words in the spaces. (If the player rolls a six, the player moves six spaces, reading the words in each space.)

2. The player says a word (or nonsense word) that rhymes with the word in the box where he or she lands. If the player lands in a box with a ★, the player says a rhyming word and then moves forward one extra square.

Alternative: The player draws a number card instead of using a die. Number cards 1–6. Make at least three cards of each number. Shuffle the cards and place the cards upside down in a draw pile.

sink

saw

★ hop

mope

mop

hope

paw

Sloth is mad. Go back to "saw."

The forest animals said, "We must save the rain forest! We must get Sloth to stop eating so fast."

Good luck getting to "Stop."

wink

mind

Stop

★ grow

kind

show

"Slow down," said Turtle. Go back to "mind."

think

Unit 42 Activity 1
For use after Exercise 1 and Story 1

Name _____

Story Comprehension
Chapter 1, Something Strange

1 **The story tells a lot about Carlos.** List three things that tell about Carlos.

Carlos the Curious

_____

_____

_____

2 **The story says, "George looked discouraged and shrugged his shoulders." Who do you think has a problem?**

○ I think Carlos the Curious has a problem.

○ I think George has a problem. He looks discouraged.

○ I think the genie in the howling desert has a problem.

3 **Who is George?** (Start with *George is . . .*)

_____

_____

4 **Where does the story take place?**

The story takes place _____

○ in a big city   ○ in a rain forest   ○ in the country

5 **Someone who is curious . . .**

○ asks many questions.

○ eats a lot and is greedy.

Name _____

Story Comprehension
Chapter 2, My First Case

1 **Who has the problem in this story?** (What is the answer? Start your sentence with *George* . . .)

_____

2 **Describe George.**

○ George is Carlos's friend. George doesn't like to talk a lot.

○ George is Carlos's dad. George is 40 years old.

3 **Describe Carlos.**

○ Carlos is a big brown bear. Carlos growls a lot.

○ Carlos is George's friend. Carlos wants to be a detective.

4 **Why has Carlos decided he will be a great detective?**

○ He will be a great detective because he is curious and likes
   to ask questions.

○ He will be a great detective because he growls a lot.

5 **What is the problem? The problem is . . .**

○ Carlos can't find his helmet.   ○ George lost his bicycle key.

○ big   ○ big   ○ happy   ○ happy
○ little   ○ little   ○ sad   ○ sad

6 **The opposite of *big* is _____. The opposite of *happy* is _____.**

Name _____

Sentence Jumble

Use the words in each box to make a sentence. Start each sentence with a capital letter. End each sentence with a period.

was curious Carlos	_____ _____

lost his key George	_____ _____

wants George his key	_____ _____

many questions asked Carlos	_____ _____

Read the sentences. Do they make sense?

Name _____

Story Comprehension
Chapter 3, The Case of the Missing Key

1 **What is George's problem?** (Who has the problem? Start your answer with *George* . . .)

_____

_____

2 **Who wants to help George? Why does this person want to help him?**

○ Carlos wants to help George because he is curious and likes to search
for answers.

○ Camel wants to help George because he learned to work hard.

3 **Complete the sentences below.**

• If George finds his key, ➡ then he can unlock his bicycle _____

• If George can unlock his bicycle lock, ➡ then he can ride_____

• If George can ride his bike, ➡ then he won't look funny wearing

a _____

4 **Where do you think Carlos and George should look for the key? Make a list.**

• _____

• _____

• _____

5 **Do you think the problem will be solved?**

○ yes   ○ no

Unit 42 Activity 5
For use after Exercise 3 and Story 3

Name _____

Main Idea and Supporting Details

Carlos, Country Detective

Carlos lives in the country near a small town. He is eight years old, and he is a detective. When something is missing, Carlos helps find it. Carlos helped his sister find her missing doll. He helped his father find his missing hammer, and he helped Miss Jones find her missing pen.

Carlos is a great detective. His door says, "Carlos the Curious, Country Detective."

1 **Who is the story about?** (Start with *The story is about . . .*)

_____

2 **One way to say the main idea is "Carlos is a great detective."**

Carlos helped his sister find her _____

He helped his father find his _____

He helped Miss Jones _____

3 **What's one way to say the main idea?** (Write a complete sentence.)

_____

4 **Write at least two sentences about Carlos.**

_____

_____

_____

Unit 42 Activity 6
For use after Exercise 4 and Story 4

Name _____

Visualizing and Illustrating
Chapter 4, More Questions

Read and illustrate the story below.

1 Carlos, his father, mother, and three sisters live in a house in the country.	**2** Carlos's best friend, George, lost his bicycle key.
3 Carlos wrote down many clues in his notebook.	**4** At the end of the chapter, George turned his pocket inside out.

5 A clue: George had a big _____

⚪ hole in his pocket   ⚪ hole in his helmet

6 What do you think happened to the key? _____

_____

Name _____

Main Idea and Supporting Details

George

George is Carlos's best friend. He is eight years old. George helps Carlos find things, but he really likes to ride his bike. George likes to ride his bike to school. He likes to ride his bike to the store. George likes to ride his bike when he has free time. George even likes to race his bike on Saturdays.

1 **Who is the story about?** (Write a complete sentence.)

_____

2 **Where does George like to ride his bike? He likes to ride . . .**

- _____

- _____

3 **What is the *whole* story about?**

    ○ George likes to race on Saturdays.

    ○ George likes to ride his bike.

    ○ George is three years old.

Name _____

Characterization

Curious Carlos

Someone who is curious asks many questions. Someone who is curious likes to inspect things.

1 Carlos and George were best friends.
   Did that make Carlos curious?   yes   no

2 Carlos asked George many questions about his lost key.
   Did that make Carlos curious?   yes   no

3 Carlos inspected a termite nest, an anthill, a rotten old log, and under a rock.
   Did that show Carlos was curious?   yes   no

4 Carlos wrote his mom a note.
   Did that make him curious?   yes   no

You should have two "yes" answers.

Unit 42 Activity 9
For use after Exercise 5 and Story 5

Name _____

Alphabetical Order and My Picture Dictionary

B
C
E
F
H
I
K
L
N
O
Q
R
T
U
W
X
Z

curi____

detecti__

ke_

1. Fill in the missing letters of the alphabet.
   Complete the words in the second column and then read them.
2. For each word, read and complete the definition. Then, complete the sentence
   or write a new sentence using the word.
3. Draw a picture of the word in the box.

curious
Someone who is curious asks a lot
of questions.

Carlos was _____

_____

_____

detective
A detective is someone whose

_____ is to look for things
or people.

A detective is _____
who helps solve a mystery.

key
A key is something that is used to
open a lock.

_____

_____

Name _____

Story Map
Carlos the Curious

★◆ INTRODUCTION

Setting • Write where the story took place.

Where

[ ]

Main Character • Write who the story is about and something about the character.

_____ _____

● BEGINNING • Write how the story started.

One day _____

_____

Write about the problem.

George had lost _____

_____

■ MIDDLE • Action

1   Carlos asked George _____

2   Carlos wrote down the _____

3   The boys went to school to find _____

▲ END • Conclusion

George had a big hole in his pocket. Carlos and George found the missing

key in George's _____

Unit 42 Activity 11
For use after Exercise 6 and Story 7

Name _____

Written Retell
Carlos the Curious

★◆ INTRODUCTION

Write where the story took place. Introduce and describe the main character.

_____

_____

_____

● BEGINNING • Write how the story started and what the problem was.

_____

_____

_____

■ MIDDLE • Write what Carlos and George did to solve the problem.

_____

_____

_____

▲ END • Write how the story ended.

_____

_____

STORY RESPONSE • Start with *I liked the story because . . .* or *I didn't like the story because . . .*

_____

_____

Name _____

Rhyming Words

Fill in the bubble next to the word or words that rhyme. The first one is done for you.

1. bought	● brought	○ enough	● thought
2. slow	○ blow	○ grew	○ grow
3. saw	○ so	○ draw	○ claw
4. new	○ now	○ few	○ night
5. face	○ pack	○ space	○ place

Rhyming Poem

Read each sentence and find the word that rhymes with the underlined word and makes sense. Fill in the bubble and write the word on the line.

1 **Carlos's teacher said, "Let's play a game.**

What is this animal's _____?"
○ big   ○ tame   ○ name

2 **This pet doesn't have a cage,**

and it cannot read a _____.
○ book   ○ paper   ○ page

3 **I'm thinking of a pet that has no paws**

and no _____."
○ space   ○ claws   ○ face

4 **George said, "I think it's a bat."**

Carlos said, "Perhaps it's a _____."
○ fish   ○ dog   ○ cat

5 **Then the teacher said, "It goes swish, swish."**

So we all said, "It must be a _____!"
○ horse   ○ cow   ○ fish

Name _____

Story Comprehension
Chapter 1, The Lost Pearls

1 **The story tells a lot about Maya. List three things that describe Maya.**

If you wish to write more, draw an extra line.

Maya the Magnificent

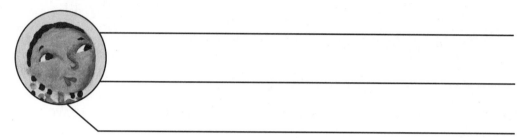

_____

_____

_____

2 **Who has a problem?**

○ Maya the Magnificent has a problem.

○ Mrs. J has a problem.

○ Bruce, Maya's little brother, has a problem.

3 **What is Mrs. J's problem?** (Who is the question about? Yes, the question is about Mrs. J. Start your answer with *Mrs. J . . .*)

_____

4 **Where does the story take place?**

The story takes place _____

○ in a house   ○ in an apartment   ○ in a school

5 **What does "Maya the Magnificent" mean?**

○ Maya the Girl   ○ Maya the Detective   ○ Maya the Great

Unit 43 Activity 2
For use after Exercise 2 and Story 2

Name _____

Story Comprehension
Chapter 2, Bruce

1 **Who has the problem in this story?** (What is the answer? Start your sentence with *Mrs. J . . .*)

_____

2 **Describe Maya.**

○ Maya the Magnificent is a city detective. She is nine years old.

○ Maya the Magnificent is a schoolgirl. She is one hundred years old.

3 **Describe Mrs. J.**

○ Mrs. J is an old man who lives in an apartment building. He wears a red hat.

○ Mrs. J is Maya's friend. She is old, and she usually has a big smile for Maya.

4 **Describe Bruce.**

○ Bruce is Maya's little sister. She is six years old.

○ Bruce is Maya's little brother. He is six years old.

5 **What is the problem? Mrs. J has . . .**

○ lost her pearls.   ○ lost her marbles.

6 **Which is up? Which is down? Which is a child? Which is an adult?**

○ down   ○ down   ○ child   ○ child
○ up   ○ up   ○ adult   ○ adult

7 **The opposite of *down* is** _____. **The opposite of *child* is** _____.

Unit 43 Activity 3
For use as appropriate

Name _____

Following Directions
Table of Contents

1 Look at the Table of Contents. Draw a circle around the picture of the main character.

2 Underline the name of Chapter 2.

3 Find "Chapter 4, No Smile." Draw an X on the word "Smile."

4 What page is "The Pink Box" on?

    ○ 41
    ○ 32
    ○ 47

5 Circle the word that means great. (It is a long word that begins with **M**.)

6 Your story is called "Maya the Magnificent." This story could also be called . . .

    ○ "The Case of the Missing Ring"
    ○ "The Case of the Missing Pearls"

TABLE OF CONTENTS
UNIT 43 • City Detective

Maya the Magnificent

Planning Assistance: See Daily Lesson Planning for scheduling.

33

Name _____

Story Comprehension
Chapter 3, The New Case

1 **Where does the story take place?** (Start with *The story takes place . . .*)

_____

_____

2 **The opposite of *happy* is** _____ .

     ○ happy   ○ happy
     ○ unhappy   ○ unhappy

3 **Why didn't Mrs. J smile? What was the problem?**
     ○ Mrs. J didn't smile because she had lost her pearls. Mrs. J was unhappy.
     ○ Mrs. J didn't smile because she had a rock in her shoe. Mrs. J
       was unhappy.

4 **Complete the sentences below.**

     • Mrs. J lost her pearls, ⟶ so Mrs. J was _____

     • If Maya finds the pearls, ⟶ then Mrs. J will pay her _____

5 **Make a list of the places you think Maya and Bruce should look for the pearls.**

     • _____

     • _____

     • _____

Name _____

Main Idea and Supporting Details

Maya, City Detective

Maya lives in a big city. She is nine years old, and she is a detective. When something is missing, Maya helps find it. Maya helped her best friend, Ann, find her missing hamster. Maya helped her mother find her missing flower seeds, and she helped Mr. Miller find his missing hat. Maya is a great detective. Her door says, "Maya the Magnificent, City Detective."

1 **Who is the story about?** (Start with *The story is about . . .*)

_____

2 **One way to say the main idea is "Maya is a great detective."**

Maya helped her friend, Ann, find _____

She helped her mother find _____

She helped Mr. Miller _____

3 **What's another way to say the main idea?** (Start your sentence with *Maya . . .*)

_____

4 **Write at least two sentences about Maya.**

_____

_____

_____

Name _____

Alphabetical Order and My Picture Dictionary

A
B

apart_____

ci___

detecti___

E
F

I
J

M
N

Q
R

U
V

Y
Z

1. Fill in the missing letters of the alphabet.
   Complete the words in the second column and then read them.
2. For each word, read the definition. Then write a new sentence using each word.
3. Draw a picture of the word in the box.

apartment
An apartment is a place where people live.
Write a sentence.

_____

_____

city
A city is a place where many people live and work.
Write a sentence.

_____

_____

detective
A detective is someone whose job is to look for things or people.
Write a sentence.

_____

_____

Name _____

Main Idea and Supporting Details

Bruce

Bruce is Maya's little brother. He is six years old. Bruce is small and quick. Bruce helps Maya find things, but he really likes to go to the park. Bruce likes to play catch, and he likes to bat a ball. Bruce really likes the game of baseball.

Bruce doesn't want to be a detective. He wants to be a great ball player. Bruce says he should be called "Bruce the Magnificent."

1 **Who is the story about?** (Start with *The story is about . . .*)

_____

2 **Who is Bruce?**

○ Maya's best friend   ○ Maya's big brother   ○ Maya's little brother

3 **List three things Bruce likes to do.**

- _____

- _____

- _____

4 **What is the *whole* story about?**

○ Bruce wants to be a great ball player.

○ Bruce wants to be a great detective.

Unit 43 Activity 8
For use as appropriate

Name _____

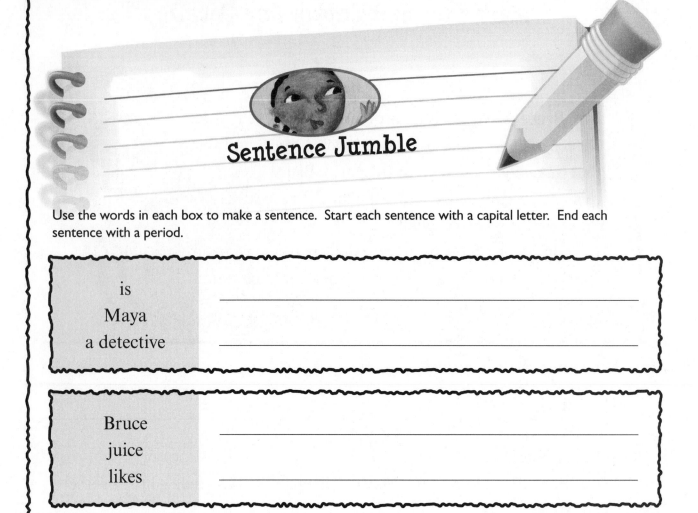

Sentence Jumble

Use the words in each box to make a sentence. Start each sentence with a capital letter. End each sentence with a period.

is Maya a detective	_____ _____

Bruce juice likes	_____ _____

lost her pearls Mrs. J	_____ _____

was a it mystery	_____ _____

Read the sentences. Do they make sense?

Name _____

Characterization and Vocabulary

The Clue: Mrs. J calls teeth "pearls" because . . .

○ teeth are white, just like pearls.

○ teeth grow in oysters.

Maya the Magnificent

Detectives are good at finding missing things and solving problems. Good detectives are curious. They ask questions. They inspect things, and they think about clues.

1 Maya wore beads in her hair.
　　Did that make Maya a good detective?　yes　　　no

2 Maya had pearly white teeth.
　　Did that make Maya a good detective?　yes　　　no

3 Maya inspected Mrs. J's apartment.
　　Did that make Maya a good detective?　yes　　　no

4 Maya thought carefully about
Mrs. J's pearly whites.
　　Did that make Maya a good detective?　yes　　　no

You should have two "yes" answers.

Name _____

Story Map
Maya the Magnificent

♦ INTRODUCTION

Main Character • Write who the story was about and something about the character.

_____   _____
                       _____

Setting • Write where the story took place.

```
┌──────────────────────────────────────────────────────┐
│                                                        │
│                                                        │
└──────────────────────────────────────────────────────┘
```

● BEGINNING • Write about the problem.

Old Mrs. J _____

_____

■ MIDDLE • Action

1 _____ and _____ were on the case.

2 They thought they were looking for _____

3 They inspected _____

4 The clue: Mrs. J wasn't missing her necklace.

She was _____

■ END • Conclusion

Maya and Bruce found Mrs. J's false teeth in the _____
   ○ trash   ○ green box   ○ refrigerator

Name _____

Written Retell
Maya the Magnificent

♦ INTRODUCTION • Write who the main character was and where she lived. Then write at least two sentences that describe Maya.

_____

_____

_____

_____

● BEGINNING • Write what the problem was and how the story began.

_____

_____

_____

■ MIDDLE • Action Write at least three sentences that tell how Maya and Bruce solved the problem. You may wish to add details that weren't on the story map.

_____

_____

_____

_____

_____

■ **END** • Write how the story ended.

_____

_____

_____

STORY RESPONSE • Start with *I liked the story because . . .* or *I didn't like the story because . . .*

_____

_____

_____

ILLUSTRATION • Draw a picture of the story in the box.

Unit 44 Activity 1
For use after Exercise 1 and Story 1

Name _____

Story Comprehension
Nate the Great, Part 1

1 **Write the main character's name in the circle. List three things that describe Nate the Great.**

_____

_____

_____

2 **In the story, Nate says, "Stay right where you are. Don't touch anything. DON'T MOVE." Why did he say this to Annie?**

  ○ Nate wanted Annie to act like a rock.

  ○ Nate didn't want Annie to touch anything that might be a clue.

3 **Do you know what Annie's problem is?** (Who is the question about? Yes, it's about Annie. Start your sentence with *Annie* . . .)

_____

4 **Where is Nate going to look for clues?** (What is the question about? Yes, it's about where Nate is going. Start your sentence with *Nate is going* . . .)

_____

_____

  ○ crazy   ○ to Annie's house   ○ to school

5 **Why is Nate called "Nate the Great?" What does he do?**

  ○ Nate is a great detective. He finds things.

  ○ Nate watches hours and hours of TV.

Unit 44 Activity 2
For use after Exercise 2 and Story 2

Name _____

Story Comprehension
Nate the Great, Part 2

1 **Who has the problem in this story?** (What is the answer? Start your sentence with *Annie* . . .)

_____

2 **Describe Nate the Great.**
- ○ Nate is great. He is a detective who works alone.
- ○ Nate is rude and lazy. He never helps anyone with anything.

3 **Describe Annie.**
- ○ Annie has pink hair. She really likes pink bubble gum.
- ○ Annie has brown hair and brown eyes. She really likes yellow.

Trapdoor	Secret Passage
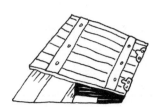	
A trapdoor is a secret door in the floor.	A secret passage is a hidden place behind a wall or bookshelf.

4 **Will Nate find the missing picture under a trapdoor?**   ○ yes   ○ no

5 **Why not?**
- ○ Nate is afraid of trapdoors.
- ○ There aren't any trapdoors in Annie's house.

6 **Will Nate find the missing picture in a secret passage?**   ○ yes   ○ no

7 **Why not?**
- ○ There isn't a secret passage in Annie's house.
- ○ Nate is afraid of secret passages.

Unit 44 Activity 3
For use after Exercise 2 and Story 2

Name _____

Sentence Jumble

Use the words in each box to make a sentence. Start each sentence with a capital letter. End each sentence with a period.

| many questions Nate asked | _____ _____ |

| was curious Nate | _____ _____ |

| Nate was a detective | _____ _____ |

★ You can make the sentence more interesting. Add the word "great."

Nate was a _____ detective.

Unit 44 Activity 4
For use after Exercise 3 and Story 3

Name _____

Story Comprehension
Nate the Great, Part 3

1 **What is Annie's problem?**

_____

2 **Who is helping Annie and why?**

○ Nate the Great is helping Annie because he likes his job as a detective. He likes to find clues and solve cases.

○ Fang is helping Annie because he's got ants in his pants.

3 **Complete the sentences below.**

• If Nate the Great is a detective, ⟶ then he can help Annie

find her _____

• If Nate the Great finds Annie's picture, ⟶ then it won't be _____

• If Nate finds the picture, ⟶ then Nate the Great will have

solved the _____

4 **Nate has already looked for the picture all over Annie's room. Make a list of other places you think Nate should look.**

• _____

• _____

• _____

5 **Do you think the problem will be solved?**   ○ yes   ○ no

Unit 44 Activity 5
For use as appropriate

Name _____

Main Idea and Supporting Details

Great Detectives

A detective looks for missing things. Carlos, Maya, and Nate were all detectives. Carlos looked for George's missing bike key. Maya looked for Mrs. J's missing pearls. Nate the Great is looking for Annie's missing picture.

1 **What is the story about?** (Start with *The story is about . . .*)

_____

_____

2 **Make a list of the things the detectives looked for.**

• Carlos looked for George's _____

• Maya looked for Mrs. J's _____

• Nate the Great looked for _____

_____

3 **What's one way to say the main idea?**

_____

◯ Detectives are greedy and rude.
◯ Detectives look for missing things.

Unit 44 Activity 6
For use after Exercise 4 and Story 4

Name _____

Story Comprehension
Nate the Great, Part 4

1 **Why did Nate the Great think Fang buried the picture in the yard?**

    Clue 1. Fang liked to bury _____

    Clue 2. Fang could only bury the picture in the _____ because

        Fang only left the yard on a _____

2 **What did Nate the Great decide to do after he and Annie dug in the yard for two hours?** (Who is this question about? Start with *Nate the Great decided . . .*)

_____

_____

_____

3 **What did Annie and Nate the Great find in the yard?** (Who is this question about? Start with *Annie and Nate found . . .*)

_____

_____

_____

4 **What did Nate the Great want to do after he ate pancakes?**
    ○ Nate the Great wanted to take Fang for a walk.
    ○ Nate the Great wanted to talk to Rosamond.
    ○ Nate the Great wanted to play a game with Annie.

Unit 44 Activity 7
For use after Exercise 5 and Story 5

Name _____

Main Idea and Supporting Details

Clues

Clues are things that help people solve a problem or a mystery. A detective uses clues to help solve a case.

Maya the Magnificent used clues to find Mrs. J's lost teeth. Nate has several clues. He is using the clues to find out where the painting isn't. Soon he will find a clue that will help him find where the painting is.

1 **What is the story about?**

  O clues   O lost teeth   O a hat

2 **One way to say the main idea is "Clues are things that help people solve a problem or a mystery."**

Maya used clues to _____

Nate is using clues to find where _____

Soon Nate will find a clue that tells him where _____

_____

Unit 44 Activity 8
For use after Exercise 5 and Story 5

Name _____

Visualizing and Illustrating

Nate the Great, Part 5

Read each sentence and write the answer in the blank. Draw a picture in each box.

1 Draw a picture of what you think Annie's missing _____ looks like.

2 Draw a picture of Rosamond's missing _____ .

3 Draw pictures of the three characters who may have taken Annie's picture.

Fang	Rosamond	Harry

4 Did Fang take Annie's picture?   ○ yes   ○ no

5 Did Rosamond take Annie's picture?   ○ yes   ○ no

6 Who do you think took Annie's picture? (Write a complete sentence.)

_____

_____

Unit 44 Activity 9
For use after Exercise 6 and Story 6

Name _____

Alphabetical Order and My Picture Dictionary

A
C
D
F
G
I
J
L
M
O
P
R
S
U
V
X
Y

cl___

detect____

pr_d_ct

1. Fill in the missing letters of the alphabet.
   Complete the words in the second column and then read them.
2. For each word, read the definition. Then, write a new sentence using each word.
3. Draw a picture of the word in the box.

clue

A clue is something that helps solve a problem or a mystery.

Write a sentence.

_____

_____

detective

A detective is a person whose job it is to look for things or people.

Write a sentence.

_____

_____

predict

To predict is to make a good guess.

Write a sentence.

There are dark clouds. I predict

that it will _____.

I predict that it will rain.

(Draw dark clouds.)

69

Unit 44 Activity 10
For use after Exercise 6 and Story 7

Name _____

Story Map
Nate the Great

♦ INTRODUCTION

Main Character • Write who the story was about in the circle. Then write something about the character.

_____

_____

● BEGINNING • Write about the problem.

Annie _____

_____

■ MIDDLE • Action.

1 First, Nate the Great looked in _____

2 Next, Nate thought Fang may have taken the picture.

So, Nate and Annie dug _____

3 Then, Nate and Annie talked to _____

4 Finally, Nate talked to Annie's _____

■ END

Nate found Annie's picture. Harry had _____

_____

Name _____

Written Retell
Nate the Great

◆ **INTRODUCTION** • Write who the main character was. Then write at least two sentences that describe Nate.

_____

_____

_____

_____

● **BEGINNING** • Write what the problem was and how the story began.

_____

_____

_____

■ **MIDDLE • Action** Write at least three sentences that tell how Nate the Great solved the problem. You may wish to add details that weren't on the story map.

_____

_____

_____

_____

_____

_____

_____

Unit 44 Activity 11
(continued)

■ END • Write how the story ended.

_____

_____

_____

STORY RESPONSE • Start with _I liked the story because …_ or _I didn't like the story because …_

_____

_____

_____

ILLUSTRATION • Draw a picture of the story in the box.

Unit 45 Activity 1
For use after Exercise 1 and Story 1

Name _____

Story Comprehension
From Egg to Frog

1 **Write one interesting fact about frogs.** (What is question 1 about? It's about frogs, so start your sentence with *Frogs . . .*)

_____

_____

2 **The change a tadpole goes through is called a** _____

○ big laugh   ○ metamorphosis   ○ mouthful

3 **Draw each part of the life cycle of a frog.**

1. First, there is an egg.	**2.** The egg hatches and out comes a tadpole.
4. The tadpole changes into a frog. The frog can live on land.	**3.** The tadpole grows legs and develops lungs.

4 **Would you rather be a tadpole or a frog? I would rather be a** _____

because _____

Unit 45 Activity 2
For use after Exercise 2 and Story 2

Name _____

Story Comprehension
Fascinating Frog Facts

1 **Some frogs are large, like the goliath frog. Some frogs are _____,**

like the gold frog. Goliath frogs and gold frogs are _____.

     ○ the same   ○ opposites

2 **Some frogs have webbed toes. Some frogs have suckers on their toes.**

These are the toes of a . . .   These are the toes of a . . .

    ○ tree frog   ○ pond frog   ○ tree frog   ○ pond frog

3 **List three fascinating facts about frogs.** (What is item 3 about? It's about frogs, so start each of your sentences with *Frogs* or *They*.

_____

_____

_____

_____

Name _____

Opposites

1 **Which habitat is wet and which is dry?**

Desert

Rain Forest

> The opposite of _wet is dry._

○ wet   ○ dry   ○ wet   ○ dry

---

2 **Which is new? Which is old?**

> The opposite of _new is old._

○ new   ○ old   ○ new   ○ old

---

3 **Which is happy? Which is unhappy?**

○ happy   ○ unhappy   ○ happy   ○ unhappy

The opposite of *sad* is _____

The opposite of *happy* is _____

Another word for *unhappy* is _____

Unit 45 Activity 4
For use after Exercise 3 and Story 3

Name _____

Story Comprehension
Frog Habitats

1 **Where do frogs live?** (What is the question about? Start with what the question is about.)

_____

_____

2 **Some frogs live in the desert. What do frogs do in the desert?**

○ They get sun tans.   ○ They go swimming.   ○ They burrow underground.

3 **If it is hot outside, ⟶ then frogs often burrow underground.**

If it is cold outside, ⟶ then frogs often _____

○ wear a coat   ○ hibernate

4 **Write a sentence.**
Unscramble the words in the box to make a new sentence.

frogs animals are	_____ _____

5 **Write an interesting sentence.**
You can make the sentence more interesting. Add the word "fascinating."

Frogs are _____**animals.**
Now you have an interesting sentence.

Name _____

Main Idea and Supporting Details

Bullfrogs

The biggest frogs in North America are bullfrogs. Like most frogs, they are meat eaters. Bullfrogs will eat almost any animal that comes their way—insects, fish, mice, and even small birds. They sit in their ponds and wait for animals to come their way. Bullfrogs use their long, sticky tongues to catch animals.

1 **What is the story about?**

○ happy green frogs

○ big bullfrogs

○ hungry bulldogs

2 **The main idea of this whole paragraph is . . .**

○ big bullfrogs are meat eaters.

○ big bullfrogs have sticky tongues.

○ big bullfrogs sit in their ponds.

3 **What are three facts you learned about bullfrogs?**

• Bullfrogs_____

• They _____

• They _____

Name _____

Fact Summary—Frogs and Toads

Frogs and toads are related. They look the same, and they have the same life cycle. They begin as eggs. Small tadpoles hatch from the eggs. The tadpoles grow legs and lungs, and then they become adult frogs or toads.

Frogs and toads are also different. Look at the chart below to see how they are different.

	Frogs	Toads
Look like	Smooth, wet skin	Bumpy, dry skin
Legs	Long back legs	Short back legs
How they move	Jump	Hop

How Frogs and Toads Are Different

Frogs are different from toads. First, frogs have smooth, wet skin,

but toads have _____

Second, frogs have long back legs, but toads _____

_____

Third, frogs can jump, but _____

Frogs and toads are a lot alike, but they are also different.
Which would you rather be—a frog or a toad?

If I had to choose, I'd rather be a _____

frog   toad

Name _____

Rhyming Words

Fill in the bubble next to the *word* or *words* that rhyme. The first one is done for you.

1. **knew**   ● grew   ○ knock   ● new
2. **change**   ○ strange   ○ range   ○ name
3. **place**   ○ phone   ○ space   ○ race
4. **snow**   ○ knew   ○ show   ○ know
5. **saw**   ○ draw   ○ paw   ○ knob

Rhyming Poem

Read the sentence and find the word that rhymes with the underlined word and makes sense. Fill in the bubble and write the word on the line.

1 There were two little frogs

sitting on _____!
○ leaves   ○ logs   ○ chairs

2 The first little frog was blue

and that is _____.
○ hard   ○ silly   ○ true

3 The second small frog was green

and very _____.
○ orange   ○ clean   ○ old

4 The little frogs played together

in every kind of _____.
○ weather   ○ mud   ○ feather

Name _____

Story Comprehension
The Animal Kingdom

1 The world of animals is called the _____

2 The animal kingdom is made up of groups. Write the name of each animal group on the lines below.

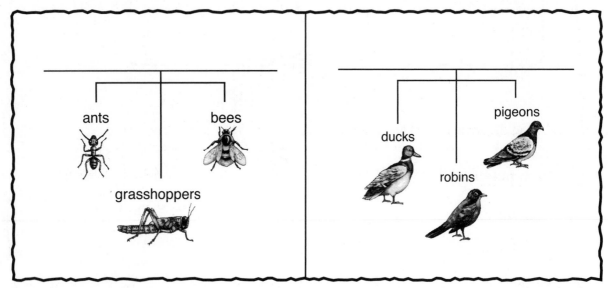

For questions 3 and 4, underline <u>what</u> the question is about. Start with that word. Number 3 is done for you.

3 What is one fact about <u>insects</u>? Insects _____

_____

4 What is one fact about birds? _____

_____

5 Do you think a frog is an insect?   ◯ yes   ◯ no

6 Do you think a frog is a bird?   ◯ yes   ◯ no

7 What kind of animal do you think a frog is?
◯ a bird   ◯ an insect   ◯ I don't think a frog is an insect or a bird.

Name _____

Main Idea and Supporting Details

Good Catch

    Frogs are good at catching insects. They have strong back legs, so they can jump quickly. Some frogs have long, sticky tongues, so they can quickly grab insects. Some frogs can even change color, so they can hide. When a frog is near, insects beware.

1 **What is this paragraph about?**

    ○ insects   ○ frogs with feathers

    ○ frogs   ○ frog legs

2 **Write "Frogs" on the line below. The sentence tells the main idea of the passage. Next, write three facts that tell about the main idea.**

Main Idea
_____are good at catching insects.

Fact 1	Fact 2	Fact 3
_____	_____	_____
_____	_____	_____
_____	_____	_____

Unit 45 Activity 10
For use after Exercise 6 and Story 6

Name _____

★Have Some Fun!

1 If a frog were a bird, it would have a beak, scaly legs, clawed toes, and feathers. Make the frog into a bird.

- Draw a beak on the frog.

- Draw scaly legs.

- Draw clawed toes.

- Now, add feathers and wings.

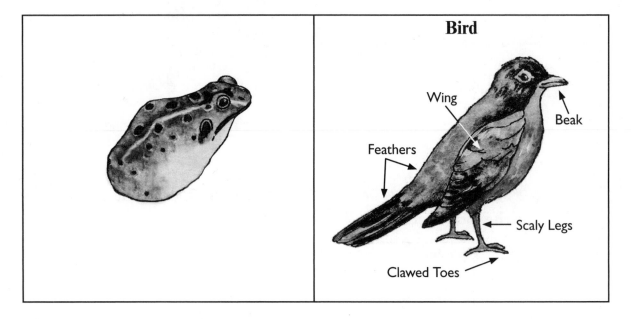

Bird

Wing

Beak

Feathers

Scaly Legs

Clawed Toes

2 Does your frog look like the bird?   ○ yes   ○ no

3 You know a lot about animals. Name one more animal in each class.

Mammals	Amphibians	Insects
• Cats	• Salamanders	• Butterflies
• Elephants	• Toads	• Flies
• _____	• _____	• _____

Unit 45 Activity 11
For use after Exercise 6 and Story 6

Name _____

Alphabetical Order and My Picture Dictionary

am _ _ ibian

1. Fill in the missing letters of the alphabet. ★ All the vowels are missing.
   Complete the words in the second column and then read them.
2. For each word, read the definition.
   Then, write a sentence using the word.
3. Draw a picture of the word in the box.

B
C
D

F
G
H   habi _ _ _

J
K
L   l _ fe cycl _
M
N

P
Q
R
S
T

V
W
X
Y
Z

amphibian

An amphibian is an animal that is cold-blooded and goes through metamorphosis.

Write a sentence.

_____

_____

life cycle

A life cycle shows the changes an animal or plant goes through during its life.

Write a sentence.

_____

_____

habitat

A habitat is the special place where plants and animals live and grow.

Write a sentence.

_____

_____

Name _____

Dear Kids,

We hope you are having fun with your new stories. You are getting really smart! You can read and understand big words—like "metamorphosis." You can read long stories. You also know a lot of facts about the world. Ask an adult if they know what a caecilian (suh-SILL-yen) is.

We hope you'll write to us. We'd love to hear what you think about *Read Well Plus*.

Sincerely,

Mrs. Sprick   Mrs. Jones

Mrs. Sprick   Mrs. Jones

Dear Mrs. Sprick and Mrs. Jones,

My <u>two</u> favorite stories were . . .

○ How the Chipmunk Got His Stripes   ○ Maya the Magnificent
○ How the Camel Got His Hump   ○ Nate the Great
○ Why the Sloth Is Slow   ○ Frogs, Toads, and
○ Carlos the Curious   Their Relatives

I liked the story about _____ because

_____

I think *Read Well Plus* is _____ because

_____

Someday, I would like to read about _____

Sincerely,

Unit 46 Activity 1
For use after Exercise 1 and Story 1

Name _____

Story Comprehension
A List, Part 1

1 **Who are the main characters?** (Who is the question about? Start your sentence with *The main characters are . . .*)

_____

_____

2 **What did Toad do when he woke up?**
   ○ He took a bubble <u>bath</u>.
   ○ He wrote a list of things to do.

3 **Make a list of the things you will do tomorrow.** (You may want to look at Toad's list.)

• <u>Wake up</u> _____

• _____

• _____

• _____

• _____

• _____

• _____

• _____

• <u>Go to sleep</u> _____

Name _____

Story Comprehension
A List, Part 2

1 **What did Toad make?** (Who is the question about? Start your sentence with *Toad . . .*)

_____

2 **What was Toad's problem?**

Toad's _____

_____

3 **What did Toad do to get his list back?**
   ○ He didn't do anything because it wasn't on his list.
   ○ He sat down and said, "Hee, hee. How funny!"

4 **Frog showed he was a good friend by . . .**
   ○ running after the list.
   ○ crying.

5 **At the end, Frog and Toad . . .**
   ○ finally went to sleep because Toad remembered it was on his list.
   ○ finally had a great supper because they were hungry.

6 **I think Toad was** _____ **because he** _____

_____

(For fun, go back to the list you made yesterday and cross off the things you've done.)

Unit 46 Activity 3
For use after Exercise 2 and Story 2

Name _____

Rhyming Words

Fill in the bubbles next to the *word* or *words* that rhyme. The first one is done for you.

1. knew	● grew	○ knock	● new
2. toad	○ road	○ range	○ name
3. coat	○ boat	○ throat	○ race
4. true	○ saw	○ show	○ blue
5. eat	○ draw	○ meat	○ knob

Rhyming Poem

Read the sentence and find the word that rhymes with the underlined word and makes sense. Fill in the bubble and write the word on the line.

1 **Toad said, "Let's talk**

while we go for a _____."
○ drive   ○ walk   ○ swim

2 **Toad sang a song**

that was very _____.
○ hard   ○ fast   ○ long

3 **Toad said, "I will make**

a great big _____!"
○ cake   ○ garden   ○ cookie

4 **Frog and Toad had fun**

when they were in the _____.
○ rain   ○ mud   ○ sun

Name _____

Main Idea and Supporting Details

Frog Adaptations

Frogs are very good at adapting to different habitats. In places where it gets very cold, frogs hibernate for the winter. In places where it gets very hot and dry, frogs burrow underground. Frogs have adapted so well to different habitats that they have lived on Earth since the dinosaurs.

1 **What is this paragraph about?**

○ frightening fish

○ colorful insects

○ frogs

2 **The main idea of this whole paragraph is . . .**

○ frogs are great at catching insects.

○ frogs are good at adapting to different habitats.

○ frogs are dinosaurs.

3 **When it is cold, ⟶ frogs . . .**

○ wear socks. ○ jump quickly. ○ hibernate.

4 **When it is hot, ⟶ frogs . . .**

○ eat ice cream. ○ burrow underground. ○ lick their noses.

Name _____

Sentence Jumble

Use the words in each box to make a sentence. Start each sentence with a capital letter and end each sentence with a period.

| toad a garden wanted | _____ _____ |

| planted toad seeds | _____ _____ |

| a problem had toad | _____ _____ |

| wouldn't his seeds grow | _____ _____ |

Read the sentences. Do they make sense?

Unit 46 Activity 6
For use after Exercise 4 and Story 4

Name _____

Story Map
The Garden

◆ **INTRODUCTION • Main Characters** Write the name of the second character in the empty circle.

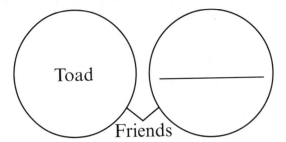

● **BEGINNING • Goal** The story started with Toad visiting Frog's garden. What did Toad want?

_____

_____

■ **MIDDLE • Problem ——→ Action**

1 Toad planted seeds, but _____

2 Toad yelled at the seeds, but _____

Write two other things that Toad did.

3 _____

_____

4 _____

_____

▲ **END • Conclusion** Explain what happened at the end.

_____

Name _____

Written Retell
The Garden

◆ **INTRODUCTION • Main Characters** Introduce Frog and Toad. Write something about them.

_____

_____

_____

● **BEGINNING • Goal** Write what Toad wanted after he saw Frog's garden.

_____

_____

_____

■ **MIDDLE • Problem ⟶ Action** Write about Toad's problem and what he did about it.

_____

_____

_____

_____

▲ **END • Conclusion** Write what happened at the end.

_____

_____

_____

RESPONSE • Start with *I liked the story because . . .* or *I didn't like the story because . . .*

_____

_____

_____

Name _____

Main Idea and Supporting Details

A Good Friend

Toad's friend, Frog, is always willing to help. Toad was very upset because his list blew away. Frog ran after the list for Toad. When Frog couldn't find the list, Frog helped Toad by sitting with him. When Toad wanted  a garden, Frog gave Toad seeds to start the garden. I think Frog is a good friend. I think Frog is a great friend. What do you think?

Main Idea

_____ is a good friend because he is always willing to help.

Frog helped Toad by	Frog helped Toad by	Frog helped Toad by
_____	_____	_____
_____	_____	_____
_____	_____	_____
_____	_____	_____

If Toad lost the key to his house, what do you think Frog would do?

_____

_____

Unit 46 Activity 9
For use after Exercise 5 and Story 5

Name _____

Alphabetical Order and My Picture Dictionary

1. Fill in the missing letters of the alphabet. All the vowels are missing. Complete the words in the second column and then read them.
2. For each word, read and complete the definition. Then, write a new sentence using the word.
3. Draw a picture of the word in the box.

B	
C	
D	
F	fr _ _
G	
H	
J	
K	
L	
M	
N	
P	
Q	
R	
S	
T	to _ _
V	
W	will po _ _ _
X	
Y	
Z	

frog
A frog is an amphibian.
Add at least one fact.

_____

_____

toad
A toad is _____

_____

Add at least one fact.

_____

will power
Will power means trying hard not to do something you shouldn't do.

Frog could show will power by . . .
○ not eating the cookies.
○ eating all the cookies.

Draw a picture of Frog giving the cookies away.

Name _____

Characterization

Will Power

Frog and Toad knew that they would get sick if they ate too many cookies.
They needed to use will power to stop eating the cookies.

1 **Frog tried putting the cookies in a box.**
    Did that show will power?   ○ yes   ○ no

2 **Frog tried putting the box of cookies
   up on a high shelf.**
    Did that show will power?   ○ yes   ○ no

3 **Frog gave the cookies to the birds.**
    Did that show will power?   ○ yes   ○ no

You should have three "yes" answers.

★ A Different Ending

4 **Draw a picture of Frog and Toad eating all of the cookies.**

5 **Are Frog and Toad showing will power in your picture?**   ○ yes   ○ no

Name _____

Sentence Jumble

Use the words in each box to make a sentence. End each sentence with a period.

Toad cookies baked	First, _____ _____

ate Frog and Toad many cookies	Second, _____ _____

the cookies hid they	Third, _____ _____

ate birds the cookies	Finally, _____ _____

Read the sentences. Do they make sense?

Unit 46 Activity 12
For use as appropriate

Name _____

Table of Contents

Find the Table of Contents at the front of your book, *Frog and Toad Together*.

1 What page is "A List" on?

    ○ page 4   ○ page 42   ○ page 30

2 If you wanted to find the story about Toad's garden, what page would you turn to?

    ○ page 4   ○ page 18   ○ page 30

3 Which story was about will power?

    ○ "A List"   ○ "The Garden"   ○ "Cookies"

★Favorites

You've read a lot of stories in *Read Well Plus!*

1 Who was your favorite animal character?

    ○ the foolish bear   ○ the greedy sloth

    ○ the foolish chipmunk   ○ the silly toad

    ○ the rude and lazy camel   ○ the nice frog

My favorite character was _____ because _____

_____

2 Who was your favorite detective?

    ○ Carlos the Curious   ○ Maya the Magnificent   ○ Nate the Great

My favorite character was _____

because _____

Unit 47 Activity 1
For use after Exercise 1 and Story 1

Name _____

Story Comprehension
Chapter 1, The Problem

1 **Have you ever been on a field trip?**   ○ yes   ○ no

2 **Describe your favorite field trip.** (What is item 2 about? It's about your favorite field trip, so start your answer with *My favorite field trip was . . .*)

_____

_____

3 **Who are the main characters in this story?**
   ○ two amphibians—Asha and Maria
   ○ two detectives—Asha and Maria
   ○ two friends—Asha and Maria

4 **Where is the class going?**
   ○ on a field trip to a zoo
   ○ on a field trip to a park
   ○ on a field trip to an asteroid mine

5 **Where do you think Asha's problem is?**
   ○ in her backpack   ○ at home   ○ in the refrigerator

★6 **Look in the glossary. Find the word "rescue." Copy the definition.**

_____

_____

7 **What do you predict will happen in "A Problem in a Backpack"?**

   I predict that _____

Unit 47 Activity 2
For use after Exercise 2 and Story 2

Name _____

Story Comprehension
Chapter 2, Asha's Secret

1 **What was in Asha's backpack?** (What is item 1 about? It's about what was in the backpack. A problem was in the backpack, so start your answer with *A problem was . . .*)

_____

2 **A funny thing happened in this chapter. We found out that . . .**

○ the teacher was a robot.

○ the kids were on a field trip.

3 **Look at the picture on page 11. Describe the children's teacher.** (Item 3 is about the children's teacher. Think about how you will start your answer. Start with *The children's teacher was . . .* Write two sentences about the robot.)

_____

_____

4 **What was the problem?**

○ The problem was an alien—a little animal from someplace in space.

○ The problem was an alien—a dinosaur from long ago.

○ The problem was false teeth in the backpack.

5 **Think about an alien from space. What do you think a space alien would look like? Draw a picture in the box. Don't peek in your book!**

Name _____

★Multisyllabic Words—Big Words

Put your hand flat under your chin. Read the first word. Each time your jaw drops, you are reading a syllable. Read each word in the list below. Count and mark the number of syllables in each word. The first one has been done for you.

1. **wonder** ○ 1 syllable ● 2 syllables ○ 3 syllables
2. **wonderful** ○ 1 syllable ○ 2 syllables ○ 3 syllables
3. **back** ○ 1 syllable ○ 2 syllables ○ 3 syllables
4. **backpack** ○ 1 syllable ○ 2 syllables ○ 3 syllables
5. **excite** ○ 1 syllable ○ 2 syllables ○ 3 syllables
6. **excitement** ○ 1 syllable ○ 2 syllables ○ 3 syllables

Rhyming Poem

Read the sentence and find the word that rhymes with the underlined word and makes sense. Fill in the bubble and write the word on the line.

1 If I meet a living thing from space,

I hope it has a happy _____.
○ smile   ○ look   ○ face

2 My alien would lay eggs

and have six _____.
○ babies   ○ legs   ○ eyes

3 If I met an alien, I would say "Hey,

I hope you will _____."
○ swim   ○ race   ○ stay

4 If I met an alien, it would be a treat

that couldn't be _____.
○ beat   ○ met   ○ eaten

Name _____

Main Idea and Supporting Details

The Octopus

An octopus is a strange-looking animal that lives under the sea. It has a big, soft body with no bones. An octopus has eight long tentacles that stretch from its body. Suckers cover the underside of these long arms. An octopus is at home in its deep sea habitat. However, if an octopus came to visit you, it would be an alien in your home.

1 **What is this paragraph about?**

○ an octopus

○ eight long tentacles

○ a deep sea habitat

2 **The main idea of this whole paragraph is . . .**

○ an octopus is a strange-looking animal that lives under the sea.

○ an octopus is a fish that lives in a backpack.

○ an octopus has no bones.

3 **If an octopus was deep in the sea, ⟶ it would be . . .**

○ an amphibian.   ○ comfortable.   ○ an alien.

4 **If an octopus was in your home, ⟶ it would be . . .**

○ an alien.   ○ happy.   ○ comfortable.

5 **Describe an octopus.**

_____

_____

Unit 47 Activity 5
For use after Exercise 3 and Story 3

Name _____

Sentence Jumble

Use the words in each box to make a sentence. Start each sentence with a capital letter and end each sentence with a period.

Asha a problem had	_____ _____

was the problem greedy	_____ _____

the problem was a ball	_____ _____

You can make the sentence more interesting by adding a word that describes the ball. Add the word "wrinkly" to make the sentence more interesting.

The problem was a _____ ball.

Read the sentences. Do they make sense?

Unit 47 Activity 6
For use after Exercise 4 and Story 4

Name _____

Visualizing and Illustrating
Chapter 4, A Bigger Problem

Read and illustrate the story below.

1 Asha and Maria's class was going on a field trip to the asteroid mine.	**2** Asha found a problem and put it in her backpack. Asha brought the problem onto the space shuttle.
3 The problem ate Asha's shoes and air tank.	**4** The teacher stretched its neck out until its head was right above the girls.

5 Can you predict what will happen next?

I predict that _____

_____

Unit 47 Activity 7
For use as appropriate

Name _____

Alphabetical Order and My Picture Dictionary

1. Fill in the missing letters of the alphabet. All the vowels are missing.
2. Fill in the blanks in the second column and then read the words. For each word, read the definition. Then, write a new sentence for "habitat" and "robot."
3. Finally, draw a picture of the word in the box.

B
C
D
F
G
H   habi____
J
K
L
M
N
P
Q
R   _ _ _ _ _
S
T
V
W
X
Y
Z

alien

An alien is a living thing from a different habitat. A camel would be an alien to the wet rain forest because camels do not live in wet habitats.

habitat

A habitat is the special place an animal or plant lives.

Write a sentence.

_____

_____

robot

A robot is a tool made by people. Robots can do some of the things that people can do.

Write a sentence.

_____

_____

Name _____

Main Idea and Supporting Details

Jellyfish

Jellyfish are interesting animals that live in the sea. Jellyfish have no bones, clear bodies, and no brains. Jellyfish have hundreds of tentacles that sting and catch food. Jellyfish are at home in their deep sea habitat. However, if a jellyfish were put on the moon, it would be an alien.

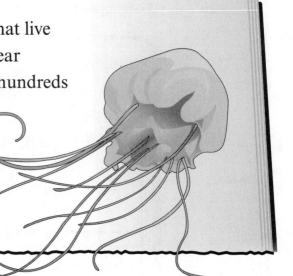

1 **What is the whole paragraph about?**

  ○ tentacles   ○ brains   ○ jellyfish

2 **Write "Jellyfish" on the line below. The sentence tells the main idea of the passage. Next, write three facts that tell about the main idea. There are more than three facts. Pick your favorites.**

Main Idea
_____ are interesting animals that live in the sea.

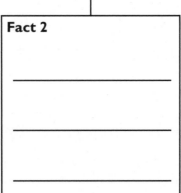

Fact 1	Fact 2	Fact 3
_____	_____	_____
_____	_____	_____
_____	_____	_____
_____	_____	_____

Name _____

★Story Completion

Our class went on a field trip to the moon. There was no air on the moon, so we carried air tanks on our backs. It was a great trip. We could see Earth floating in space below us. Then, we saw a fantastic sight.

1 Use the words in the box to make a sentence.

an alien	_____
us	
greeted	_____

2 Make the sentence more interesting by adding the word "bicolored" to describe the alien.

A _____ alien greeted us.

3 Choose what happens next.

The alien . . .
   ○ smiled and shook our hands.
   ○ screeched and ran away.

4 Write a sentence to end the story.

_____

Read the story. Does it make sense? Draw a picture of the bicolored alien in the box above.

Unit 47 Activity 10
For use after Exercise 6 and Story 6

Name _____

Story Map
A Problem in a Backpack

♦ **INTRODUCTION**

Main Characters • Write the name of the second character in the empty circle.
Write about both characters by filling in the blanks.

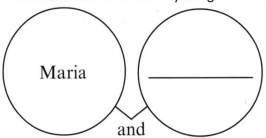

Maria   _____

and

Best _____

Lived on a _____

● **BEGINNING · Action** List three things you learned at the beginning.

- _____
  _____

- _____
  _____

- _____
  _____

■ **MIDDLE · Problem ⟶ Action**

1 The problem ate _____

2 Then the problem ate _____
If the tank exploded, the space shuttle would explode.

3 So, they sent the problem _____

▲ **END · Conclusion** Explain what happened at the end.

_____

Unit 47 Activity 11
For use after Exercise 6 and Story 6

Name _____

Written Retell
A Problem in a Backpack

♦ **INTRODUCTION · Main Characters** Introduce Maria and Asha. Write about both characters.

_____

_____

_____

_____

● **BEGINNING ·** Explain how the story started.

_____

_____

_____

■ **MIDDLE · Problem ⟶ Action** Describe what the problem did, what happened, and what they did about it.

_____

_____

_____

_____

_____

Unit 47 Activity 11
(continued)

Name _____

■ **END** • Explain what happened at the end.

_____

_____

_____

STORY RESPONSE • Start with *I liked the story because ...* or *I didn't like the story because ...*

_____

_____

_____

ILLUSTRATION • Draw a picture of the story in the box.

Unit 48 Activity 1
For use after Exercise 1 and Story 1

Name _____

Story Comprehension
Space

1 Earth is covered by a big blanket of air called the _____
   ○ metamorphosis   ○ clouds   ○ atmosphere

2 Everything beyond the Earth's atmosphere is _____
   ○ dusty   ○ cloudy   ○ space

3 Space is _____

4 This is a picture of the _____
   ○ Solar System   ○ Earth   ○ Moon

5 Write "Sun" in the box pointing to the Sun.

6 Write "Earth" in the box pointing to the planet you live on.

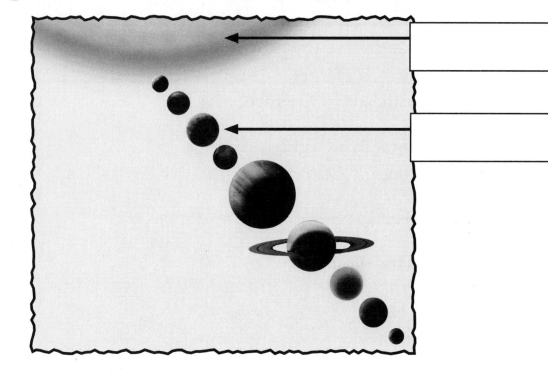

Unit 48 Activity 2
For use after Exercise 2 and Story 2

Name _____

Story Comprehension
The Earth and the Moon

1 **Why does our Earth look blue from space?**
(What is this question about? It's about why Earth looks blue. So, start your sentence with *Earth looks blue from space because . . .*)

_____

_____

_____

2 **This is a picture of** _____
○ an alien   ○ an astronaut   ○ a robot

3 **What does an astronaut wear on his back?**
○ an air tank   ○ wings   ○ an alien

4 **Draw an air tank on his back.**

5 **Would you like to live on the Moon?**
○ yes   ○ no

6 **Why?**

_____

Unit 48 Activity 3
For use as appropriate

Name _____

Multisyllabic Words–Big Words

Put your hand flat under your chin. Read the first word. Each time your jaw drops, you are reading a syllable. Read each word in the list below. Count and mark the number of syllables in each word. The first one has been done for you.

1. **asteroid**   ○ 1 syllable   ○ 2 syllables   ○ 3 syllables
2. **planet**   ○ 1 syllable   ○ 2 syllables   ○ 3 syllables
3. **voice**   ○ 1 syllable   ○ 2 syllables   ○ 3 syllables
4. **fantastic**   ○ 1 syllable   ○ 2 syllables   ○ 3 syllables
5. **astronaut**   ○ 1 syllable   ○ 2 syllables   ○ 3 syllables
6. **atmosphere**   ○ 1 syllable   ○ 2 syllables   ○ 3 syllables

Rhyming Poem

Read each item and find the word that rhymes with the underlined word and makes sense. Fill in the bubble and write the word on the line.

1   I had a smile on my <u>face</u>.

Mom said that we were traveling out into _____ .
○ race   ○ space   ○ the clouds

2   She said, "We will be going <u>far</u>

to see a bright and shining _____ ."
○ tooth   ○ star   ○ gold bar

3   Mom said, "It may get very <u>hot</u>."

I said, "That's okay. I'd rather go than _____ ."
○ not   ○ brought   ○ fly

4   Soon we were on our <u>way</u>

to that star so far _____ .
○ out   ○ away   ○ stay

Name _____

Story Comprehension
Traveling in Space

1 Look in the glossary. Find the word "atmosphere" and copy the definition.

_____

_____

2 If we go to the moon, ⟶ we must take _____

_____

○ candy and juice   ○ air, water, and food   ○ a pet

3 Where have astronauts lived?

○ on the Moon

○ on the Sun

○ on the International Space Station

4 If you were going to live on a space station, what would you take with you? Make a list of six important things.

1. _____

2. _____

3. _____

4. _____

5. _____

6. _____

Unit 48 Activity 5
For use after Exercise 3 and Story 3

Name _____

Main Idea and Supporting Details

The International Space Station

The International Space Station is a very exciting place to work. Why? Astronauts live on the Space Station for many months. They go on spacewalks. They conduct experiments, and they learn about living in space. Perhaps someday, you will be able to work in space. Perhaps someday, your whole family will be able to take a vacation in space.

1 **What is this paragraph about?**
- ○ the International Zoo
- ○ the International Space Station
- ○ a walk in space

2 **Write the topic on the line below. The sentence tells the main idea of the passage. Then write three facts that tell about your main idea.**

Main Idea
_____
is a very exciting place to work.

Fact 1	Fact 2	Fact 3
_____	_____	_____
_____	_____	_____
_____	_____	_____

Name _____

Story Comprehension
Traveling to Other Planets

1 **Where have <u>people</u> traveled to in space?** Mark two circles.

    ◯ to the Moon

    ◯ to the International Space Station

    ◯ to all the planets except Pluto

    ◯ to Pluto

2 **What are space probes?**

    ◯ spacecraft that do not carry astronauts

    ◯ spacecraft that carry astronauts

3 **Where have space probes been sent?**

    ◯ to all the planets except Pluto

    ◯ to the Sun

4 **Draw a picture of a space probe.**

Unit 48 Activity 7
For use after Exercise 4 and Story 4

Name _____

Alphabetical Order and My Picture Dictionary

B C D F G H J K L M N P Q R S T V W X Y Z

astr_nau_

Ear__

sp_c_ probe

1. Fill in the missing letters of the alphabet. All the vowels are missing.
   Then complete the words in the second column and read them.
2. For each word, read the definition. Then write a sentence using the word.
3. Draw a picture of the word in the box.

astronaut

An astronaut is a person who travels in space.

Add at least one fact about an astronaut.

_____

_____

Earth

Earth is a planet.

Add at least one fact about Earth.

_____

_____

space probe

A space probe is a spacecraft that does not carry people.

Add at least one fact about space probes.

_____

_____

Unit 48 Activity 8
For use after Exercise 5 and Story 5

Name _____

Story Comprehension
Surprises in Space

1 Look back through your book. Write three of the most interesting facts you've learned about space so far.

_____

_____

_____

_____

2 How long have people studied space through telescopes?

○ about 400 minutes   ○ about 400 years   ○ about four years

3 What is Sedna?

○ Sedna is my sister.
○ Sedna is like a planet.
○ Sedna is like the Sun.

4 Describe Sedna. Write at least two facts.

_____

_____

_____

5 Scientists have many questions about space. Write one question that you have about space.
(Start with *What, Where, How, Why* or *Is.* ★Put a question mark at the end of your question.)

_____

_____

Unit 48 Activity 9
For use after Exercise 5 and Story 5

Name _____

Paragraph Comprehension

Pluto

Nine planets circle the Sun. Pluto is the farthest planet from the Sun. People discovered Pluto about 75 years ago.

Scientists study Pluto through powerful telescopes. The planet is made of rock and covered in ice and gas.

Scientists want to learn more about Pluto. They are planning to send a space probe to the planet, but it will take more than nine years to get there.

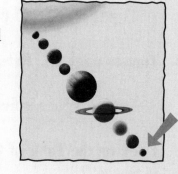

1 **What are the three paragraphs about?**

○ a dog called Pluto

○ a planet called Pluto

○ a planet with feathers

2 **What do we know about Pluto? List at least four facts.**

_____

_____

_____

_____

_____

_____

Unit 48 Activity 10
For use after Exercise 6 and Story 6

Name _____

★ Finding Information

1 Look at the Table of Contents on page 27. Where will you find the first part called "1. Space"?

     ○ page 28   ○ page 31   ○ page 34

2 Turn to page 28. Reread page 28. Then complete the sentence below.

     I think space is fascinating because space is _____

3 Look on the Table of Contents on page 27. Where will you find "3. Traveling in Space"?

     ○ page 28   ○ page 31   ○ page 34

4 Look in the glossary. Find the word "vast" and copy the definition.

_____

_____

5 Reread pages 34–36. Then write three interesting facts about the International Space Station.

_____

_____

_____

_____

_____

_____

Unit 48 Activity 11
For use after Exercise 6 and Story 6

Name _____

Fact Summary
My Notes About Space

For each of the topics below, complete the first fact.
Then write one more interesting fact.

1 **Earth and the Solar System** (You may wish to reread page 30.)

- There are _____ planets in the Solar System.

- _____

_____

2 **Our Moon** (You may wish to reread pages 32–33.)

- Twelve people have _____

- _____

_____

3 **The International Space Station** (You may wish to reread pages 34–36.)

- Astronauts are _____ on the International Space Station.

- _____

_____

4 We also learned about Pluto, Sedna, and the stars. **Challenge:** You may wish to add to your Fact Summary by writing interesting facts about Pluto, Sedna, and the stars on another piece of paper.

I think learning about space is _____ because _____

_____

Name _____

Take-Home Game
Alien in Space

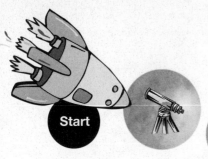

Start

Go back one space to watch the stars.

Forgot air tanks. Go back to "Start."

Materials: Game markers,
Die (or Number Cards 1–6, three of each)

Goal: To get to "Stop"

Game Directions:

This game can be played with two or three players.

1. The player rolls the die and then reads the sentence next to the number rolled. (If the player rolls a six, the player reads sentence number 6.)

2. The player moves his or her marker the number rolled on the die. (If the player rolled a six, the player moves six spaces.)

3. The player reads and follows the directions on the space.

Alternative: The player draws a number card instead of using a die.

Zoom ahead to the next stars.

Go back two spaces to avoid an asteroid.

Smile. You are safe here.

Skip one turn to rest.

Take a spacewalk. Zoom ahead two spaces.

Discover new planet. Move ahead four spaces.

Smile at alien. Go ahead two spaces.

Got lost. Lose one turn.

Stop

Make friends with the alien.

1 I have always dreamed of being an astronaut.

2 If I were an astronaut, I might travel to the moon.

3 If I were an astronaut, I might take a spacewalk.

4 Can you imagine traveling beyond the Earth's atmosphere?

5 Can you imagine taking photos in space?

6 It would be exciting to meet an alien from space!

Unit 49 Activity 1
For use after Exercise 1 and Story 1

Name _____

Story Comprehension
Millions of Years Ago

1 Write one interesting fact about dinosaurs.

_____

_____

2 Some dinosaurs were as tall as a six-story building. Imagine that! Look at the city below. It shows a six-story building. Draw a dinosaur that is as tall as the building.

3 What would you like to learn about dinosaurs? I would like to learn _____

_____

Unit 49 Activity 2
For use after Exercise 2 and Story 2

Name _____

Story Comprehension
Dinosaur Classification

	Mammals	Dinosaurs
Had backbones	Yes	Yes
Breathed air	Yes	Yes
Gave live birth to their babies	Yes	**No**
Took care of their babies	Yes	Yes
Had hair or fur	Yes	**No**

Even though dinosaurs had backbones, breathed air, and took care of their babies, dinosaurs were different from mammals.

Dinosaurs were different from mammals because they _____

_____

○ gave live birth to their babies   ○ laid eggs

Dinosaurs were different from mammals because they _____

_____

○ were covered with scaly skin   ○ were covered with hair or fur

Dinosaurs _____ mammals.
○ were   ○ were not

	Reptiles	Dinosaurs
Scaly skin	Yes	Yes
Breathed air	Yes	Yes
Laid eggs	Yes	Yes
Cold-blooded	Yes	**Maybe**

Just like other reptiles, dinosaurs had scaly skin, breathed air, laid eggs, and may have been cold-blooded. Scientists usually say dinosaurs

_____ reptiles.

○ were   ○ were not

Unit 49 Activity 3
For use as appropriate

Name _____

Multisyllabic Words–Big Words

Put your hand flat under your chin. Read a word. Each time your jaw drops, you've said a syllable. Read each word in the list below. Count and mark the number of syllables in each word. The first one is done for you.

1. **dinosaurs**	○ 1 syllable	○ 2 syllables	● 3 syllables
2. **mammals**	○ 1 syllable	○ 2 syllables	○ 3 syllables
3. **class**	○ 1 syllable	○ 2 syllables	○ 3 syllables
4. **fantastic**	○ 1 syllable	○ 2 syllables	○ 3 syllables
5. **eggs**	○ 1 syllable	○ 2 syllables	○ 3 syllables
6. **beaks**	○ 1 syllable	○ 2 syllables	○ 3 syllables

Opposites

1 **Which is the smallest dinosaur? Which is the biggest dinosaur?**

Micropachycephalosaurus   **Argentinosaurus**

○ smallest ○ biggest   ○ smallest ○ biggest

2 **Argentinosaurus and Micropachycephalosaurus are <u>opposites</u> in size.**

Argentinosaurus is the _____ dinosaur.

Micropachycephalosaurus is the _____ dinosaur.

Unit 49 Activity 4
For use after Exercise 3 and Story 3

Name _____

Story Comprehension
Dinosaur Eggs

1 **Write down the names of two animals that lay eggs.**

- _____
- _____

2 **The largest dinosaur eggs were about the size of** _____
  ○ a bus   ○ a baseball   ○ a football

3 **Just like birds, dinosaurs made** _____
  ○ spacecrafts   ○ nests   ○ lunch

4 **What did baby dinosaurs use to break out of their eggs?**
  ○ a special tooth   ○ a hammer   ○ a beak

5 **Mother dinosaurs would protect their babies while they were growing in the nest. Draw a picture of a mother dinosaur protecting her babies.**

Unit 49 Activity 5
For use after Exercise 3 and Story 3

Name _____

Main Idea and Supporting Details

The Best Guess

Dinosaurs are extinct, but scientists don't know why. Some scientists think huge volcanoes may have erupted. The volcanoes would have made the Earth too hot and then too cold. Other scientists think the dinosaurs may have become sick and died out over time. Many scientists think a huge asteroid may have hit the Earth. The crash would have made the Earth too dusty for sunlight to reach the Earth.

1 **What is this paragraph about?**

○ astronauts   ○ dinosaurs   ○ volcanoes

2 **Write the topic on the line below. The sentence tells the main idea of the passage.**

Main Idea

_____ are extinct, but scientists don't know why.

First Guess	Second Guess	Third Guess
_____	_____	_____
_____	_____	_____
_____	_____	_____
_____	_____	_____

Unit 49 Activity 6
For use after Exercise 4 and Story 4

Name _____

Story Comprehension
Dinosaur Dinner

1 Some dinosaurs were carnivores. What did they eat?

○ plants—leaves, trees, and grasses

○ animals—birds, fish, and other dinosaurs

○ junk food—hot dogs, candy, and chips

2 Look back in your book. What are some things each kind of dinosaur ate?

• Carnivores ate _____

• Herbivores ate _____

• Omnivores ate _____ and _____

3 Look back in your book. Write three of the most interesting things you've learned about dinosaurs so far.

_____

_____

_____

_____

_____

4 Scientists have many questions about dinosaurs. Write one question that you have about dinosaurs. (Start with *What, Where, How, Why,* or *Is.* Put a question mark at the end of your question.)

_____

_____

Unit 49 Activity 7
For use as appropriate

Name _____

Alphabetical Order and My Picture Dictionary

1. Fill in the missing letters of the alphabet. All the vowels are missing.
   Complete the words in the second column and then read them.
2. For each word, read the definition. Then, write a new sentence using the word.
3. Draw a picture of the word in the box.

B
C
D   d_n_saur
    _xt_nct
F   f_ss_l
G
H

J
K
L
M
N

P
Q
R
S
T

V
W
X
Y
Z

dinosaur

A dinosaur is a kind of animal
that lived 65 million years ago.

Write another sentence.

_____

_____

extinct

To be extinct is to die out.

Write another sentence.

_____

_____

fossil

A fossil is what is left of
animals and plants that lived
long ago.

Write one fact about fossils.

_____

_____

Name _____

Main Idea and Supporting Details

An Asteroid

Many scientists think a huge asteroid from space hit the Earth. They think that fires started, storms broke out, and a thick cloud of dust covered the Earth. Many scientists think that the cloud was so thick that sunlight could not get through. This would have made the Earth very dark and cold. The asteroid blast may have made the dinosaurs die out.

1 **What is the topic of this paragraph?**

     O an anteater   O an alien from space   O an asteroid

2 **Many scientists think a huge asteroid hit the Earth.**

     When the asteroid hit the Earth, ⟶ _____

     O fires started   O aliens laughed   O dinosaurs flew away

     When the asteroid hit the Earth, ⟶ _____

     _____

     O frogs croaked   O Carlos got curious   O dust clouds covered the Earth

     When the sunlight could not get through the dust clouds, . . .

     O Earth got very dark and cold.   O Earth got very mad.

3 **The main idea of this passage is many scientists think a huge asteroid hit the Earth and . . .**

     O the dinosaurs ate too much.

     O the dinosaurs died out.

Name _____

★ Note Taking
Dinosaurs

Congratulations! You know so much about dinosaurs that you can write your own report. First you are going to take notes. Then you are going to write your report using your notes.

♦ **INTRODUCTION** · Tell what your report is about.

Subject _____

Look through your book and find two dinosaur topics that you would like to write about. You can look at the Table of Contents and at the headings to help you decide what you want to write about.

■ **Topic 1** _____

■■ **Topic 2** _____

■ **MIDDLE OF YOUR REPORT · BODY** Tell facts about each topic.

■ **Topic 1** _____

Fact 1	**Fact 2**	**Fact 3**
_____	_____	_____
_____	_____	_____
_____	_____	_____
_____	_____	_____
_____	_____	_____

Unit 49 Activity 9
(continued)

■ **MIDDLE OF YOUR REPORT • BODY** *(continued)*

■■ **Topic 2** _____

Fact 1	Fact 2	Fact 3
_____	_____	_____
_____	_____	_____
_____	_____	_____
_____	_____	_____
_____	_____	_____

▲ **CONCLUSION** • List three reasons dinosaurs are interesting.

- _____

- _____

- _____

Unit 49 Activity 1o
For use after Exercise 6 as appropriate

Name _____

★Written Report: _____

♦ **INTRODUCTION** • Tell what your report is about. Introduce the subject. Then write a sentence about each topic.

_____

_____

_____

_____

_____

■ **MIDDLE • Body of the Report**

■ **Topic 1** • Introduce your first topic. Then write at least three interesting sentences.

_____

_____

_____

_____

_____

■■ **Topic 2** • Introduce your second topic. Then write at least three interesting sentences.

_____

Unit 49 Activity 1o
(continued)

_____

_____

_____

_____

▲ **CONCLUSION** • Tell why you think dinosaurs are interesting.

_____

_____

_____

_____

_____

_____

ILLUSTRATION • Draw a picture.

Unit 50 Activity 1
For use after Exercise I and Story I

Name _____

Story Comprehension
Chapter 1, The Muddy Walk

1 **What did Paul and Bobo do each day?**

    O They played catch in the park.

    O They went on long walks along the edge of the forest.

    O They walked on the Moon.

2 **Why didn't Paul want to go into the forest?** (What is this question about? It's about Paul, so start your answer with *Paul . . .*)

_____

_____

_____

3 **Paul wondered what might be lurking in the forest. He wondered if there were**

_____ **in the forest.**

    O rude camels   O purple cows   O hidden dangers

4 **At the end of this chapter, what was Paul's problem?**

    O His dog Bobo ran into the forest.

    O He ate too much and felt sick.

    O His parents turned into aliens.

5 **Predict what the Bobosaurus is. Tell what you think will happen next.**

    I predict that the Bobosaurus is _____

_____

Unit 50 Activity 2
For use after Exercise 2 and Story 2

Name _____

Story Comprehension
Chapter 2, Into the Forest

1 **Describe Alexis.**

_____

_____

2 **What was Alexis doing when Paul got to the house?**
- ○ She was brushing her teeth.
- ○ She was reading a book about dinosaurs.
- ○ She was hiding in a box.

3 **Why was Paul gasping for breath?** (What is this question about? It is about why Paul was gasping, so start your answer with *Paul was gasping for breath because . . .*)

_____

_____

4 **Alexis pulled on her boots because** _____

_____

- ○ she was afraid ants would get into her shoes
- ○ it was muddy from the rain

5 **Paul and Alexis heard strange noises in the forest. Something was lurking in the forest. What do you think it was? Draw a picture in the box.**

Unit 50 Activity 3
For use as appropriate

Name _____

Multisyllabic Words—Big Words

★ Put your hand flat under your chin. Read a word. Each time your jaw drops, you've said a syllable. Read each word in the list below. Count and mark the number of syllables in each word. The first one is done for you.

1. **surprisingly**	● 4 syllables	○ 5 syllables	○ 6 syllables
2. **imagination**	○ 4 syllables	○ 5 syllables	○ 6 syllables
3. **classification**	○ 4 syllables	○ 5 syllables	○ 6 syllables
4. **experiment**	○ 4 syllables	○ 5 syllables	○ 6 syllables
5. **International**	○ 4 syllables	○ 5 syllables	○ 6 syllables
6. **Argentinosaurus**	○ 4 syllables	○ 5 syllables	○ 6 syllables

Rhyming Poem

Read each sentence and find the word that rhymes with the underlined word and makes sense. Fill in the bubble and write the word on the line. Then read the poem.

1 **Bobo, the dog, found a nice <u>treat</u>.**

His bowl was full of a bunch of _____.
○ food   ○ meat   ○ candy

2 **Bobo wondered, "Who is the meat <u>from</u>?"**

But as he ate, his only thought was, "_____!"
○ Ick   ○ Yucky   ○ Yum

3 **Bobo ate the meat until he was <u>full</u>,**

and then he thought, "Dog food is _____!"
○ dull   ○ nice   ○ sick

4 **Bobo barked when he saw Paul <u>smile</u>,**

then Paul said, "I'll give you a treat in a _____."
○ bit   ○ while   ○ minute

Name _____

Main Idea and Supporting Details

Extinct Reptiles

Dinosaurs were reptiles. They are related to snakes, crocodiles, turtles, and lizards. In fact, the word "dinosaur" means "terrible lizard." Like other reptiles, most dinosaurs had scaly skin, laid eggs, were cold-blooded, and breathed air with their lungs.

1 **What is this paragraph about?**

   ○ dinosaurs   ○ crocodiles   ○ eggs

2 **The main idea of this whole paragraph is . . .**

   ○ dinosaurs came in all shapes and sizes.

   ○ dinosaurs were reptiles.

   ○ dinosaurs laid eggs.

★Classification

You know a lot about the animal kingdom. Fill in the blanks in the chart below by adding another bird, insect, amphibian, mammal, and reptile.

Animal Kingdom

Birds	Insects	Amphibians	Mammals	Reptiles
Robins	Bees	Frogs	Cats	Lizards

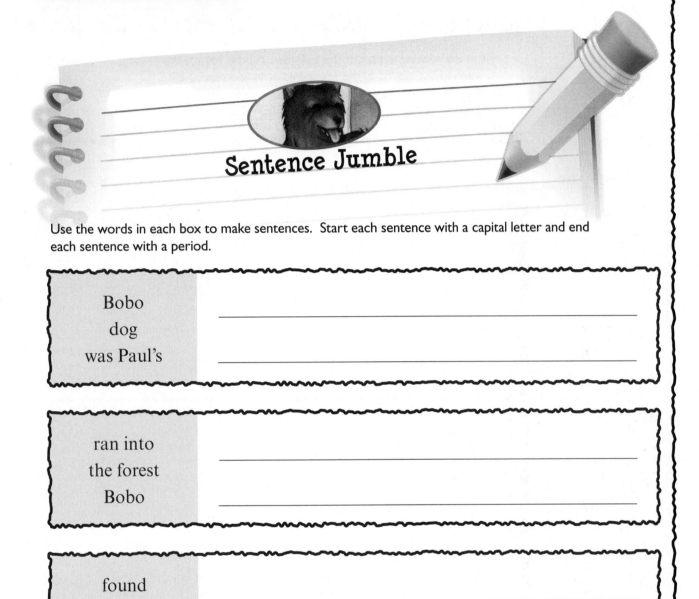

Sentence Jumble

Use the words in each box to make sentences. Start each sentence with a capital letter and end each sentence with a period.

| Bobo
dog
was Paul's | _____
_____ |

| ran into
the forest
Bobo | _____
_____ |

| found
Bobo
bones | _____
_____ |

That was a good sentence, but you can make it more interesting by adding a word that describes the bones. Add the word "huge" to make the sentence more interesting.

| Bobo
huge bones
found | _____
_____ |

Read the sentences. Do they make sense?

Unit 50 Activity 6
For use after Exercise 4 and Story 4

Name _____

Alphabetical Order and My Picture Dictionary

1. Fill in the missing letters of the alphabet. All the vowels are missing.
   Complete the words in the second column and read them.
2. For the first word, read and complete the definition.
   For the next words, write a new sentence using the word.
3. Draw a picture of the word in the box.

B
C
D   din_sau_
     ext_nc_
F   foss_ls
G
H

J
K
L
M
N

P
Q
R
S
T
V
W
X
Y
Z

dinosaur
A dinosaur was _____

_____

_____

_____

extinct
To be extinct is to no longer exist.
Write a sentence.

_____

_____

fossils
Fossils are what is left of animals
and plants that lived long ago.
Write a sentence.

_____

_____

Unit 50 Activity 7
For use after Exercise 4 and Story 4

Name _____

Visualizing and Illustrating
Chapter 4, The Big Find

Read and illustrate the story below.

1 At the beginning of the story, Bobo ran into the forest.	**2** Paul and his older sister, Alexis, went into the forest to find Bobo.
3 Paul and Alexis found Bobo at a mudslide. There were dinosaur bones poking out of the mud.	**4** Scientists came from all over the world to study the bones.

Name _____

Main Idea and Supporting Details

Scientists

Scientists are like detectives. Scientists try to find the answers to problems or puzzles. Just like detectives, scientists look for clues. They ask questions. They inspect things and take notes. Then they study the notes to find answers.

1 **The main idea of this whole paragraph is . . .**

　　○ scientists are like detectives.

　　○ an octopus lives in a backpack.

　　○ scientists ask questions.

2 **Write "Scientists" on the first line below. Then complete the sentence. The sentence tells the main idea of the passage. Next, write three details that tell about the main idea.**

> **Main Idea**
>
> _____ are like _____

Detail 1	Detail 2	Detail 3
_____	_____	_____
_____	_____	_____
_____	_____	_____
_____	_____	_____

Unit 50 Activity 9
For use after Exercise 5 and Story 5

Name _____

Have Some Fun!

1 **Imagine finding your own dinosaur! Scientists might name it after you.**

Your dinosaur would be named _____ osaurus.
                                                    (your name)

2 **Describe what your dinosaur ate.** (Remember, some dinosaurs were meat eaters [carnivores], some were plant eaters [herbivores], and some were plant and meat eaters [omnivores].)

_____

_____

3 **Describe how big your dinosaur grew to be.** (Argentinosaurus was as tall as a six-story building. Micropachysephalosaurus was as small as a cat.)

_____

_____

4 **Dinosaurs are extinct, but it is fun to imagine them returning to Earth. Draw a picture of your dinosaur visiting a city.**

Unit 50 Activity 10
For use after Exercise 6 and Story 6

Name _____

Story Map
The Bobosaurus

◆ INTRODUCTION

Main Characters • Write the names of the main characters in the empty circles. Write something about each character. Add lines if you wish to write more.

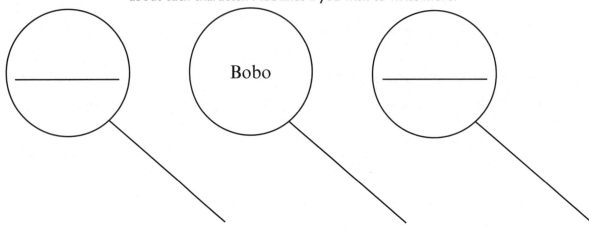

● BEGINNING • Problem Where did Bobo go in the beginning of the story?

First, _____

_____

■ MIDDLE • Action What did Paul do to solve the problem? What happened next?

1 Next, Paul ran home and _____

2 When they found Bobo, he had _____

3 Scientists _____

▲ END • Conclusion Explain what happened at the end.

_____ , the scientists named the dinosaur Bobosaurus.

○ First   ○ Next   ○ Finally

Unit 50 Activity 11
For use after Exercise 6 and Story 6

Name _____

Written Retell
The Bobosaurus

◆ **INTRODUCTION • Main Characters** Introduce Paul, Alexis, and Bobo.

_____

_____

_____

● **BEGINNING • Problem** Explain how the story started.

First, _____

_____

■ **MIDDLE • Action** What did Paul do to solve the problem? What happened next?

Next, _____

_____

_____

_____

▲ **END • Conclusion** Explain what happened at the end.

Finally, _____

_____

RESPONSE • Explain how you felt about this story.

_____

_____

Unit 50 Activity 12
For use as appropriate

Name _____

Take-Home Game
Congratulations!

Start

★★★

Go back
two spaces
to dig for
dinosaurs.

Go
forward one
space to
find Bobo.

Materials: Game markers,
 Die (or Number Cards 1–6, three of each)
Goal: To get to the "End" and have a dinosaur named after you

Game Directions:
This game can be played with two or three players.
1. The player rolls the die, reads the sentence or question next to the number rolled, and then responds.
2. The player moves his or her marker the number rolled on the die. (If the player rolled a six, the player moves six spaces.)
3. The player reads and follows the directions on the game board.

Alternative: The player draws a number card instead of using a die.

★★★

Zoom
ahead to
the next
stars.

★★★

Go back
two spaces
to avoid
mud.

Smile.
You are safe
here.

Skip one
turn to
rest.

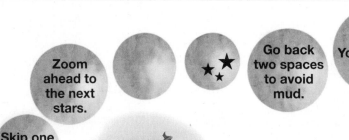

Discover a
new dinosaur.
Move to the
end.

★★

Discover
new planet.
Move ahead
four spaces.

★★★

You got
lost. Lose
one turn.

End
Dinosaur
named after
you!

★★

1 **Name three dinosaurs.**

2 **Explain how frogs and toads go through a metamorphosis.**

3 **What is a dinosaur?**

4 **Would you like to travel in space? Where would you go?**

5 **What was your favorite story in *Read Well Plus*? Explain why.**

6 **What would you like to read about next?**

144